HOW TO GET YOUR TRIVIA ON!

Pull on your phat pants, chuck on a choker, bust out your combat boots and get ready for a ton of fun with the *90s Trivia Quiz*! This book contains 601 questions over 85 rounds and is divided into 4 categories:

Each round contains questions on one side of the page with the answers printed on the reverse side. This means that the person reading the questions can also participate in the game without seeing the answers.

If playing in a group, divide into teams, or play as individuals, and nominate a host to read out the questions. You can even rotate the host each round. Choose how many rounds you want to play in total and from what categories. Each team should number and write down their answers on a piece of paper. At the end of each round, ask the teams to swap and mark the answer sheets. The team with the highest score at the end of all rounds is the winner!

For playing solo, it is best to wait to the end of each round before checking answers and to write them on separate paper, so you don't accidentally see the answers to other questions.

Booyah—it's time to get your trivia on!

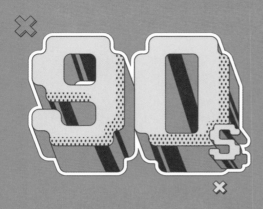

MOVIES

The 90s truly was a Titanic decade for film. Action blockbusters reigned supreme; box offices overflowed with teenage girls desperate to meet their Prinze (Jnr); and family-friendly, feel-good films flourished. Some filmmakers though started delving into the darker themes of war, politics, and human suffering. A night at the cinema was just like a box of chocolates; you never knew what you were gonna get!

Whether you were The Last Boy Scout, a Menace II Society, or even just totally Clueless back in the 90s, this round has something to have you totally buggin'. So get together your Sister Act, your Boyz n the Hood, or even just A Few Good Men, and settle down for a Jurassic night in!

From the Classics
QUESTIONS

1 The 1999 romantic comedy *10 Things I Hate About You*, starring Julia Stiles, is based on which Shakespeare play?

2 What is the name of the 1992 animated film, which stars Matthew Broderick in a voice role, whose plot is widely considered to be based on *Hamlet*?

3 Which two actors appeared as the titular star-crossed lovers in the 1996 adaptation of *Romeo and Juliet*, directed and co-written by Baz Luhrmann?

4 Which 1995 comedy starring Alicia Silverstone is a modern-day adaptation of Jane Austen's *Emma*?

5 Which actor, named after the Minnesota town in which she was born, starred as Jo in the 1994 adaptation of Louisa May Alcott's *Little Women*?

6 Rearrange the letters below to reveal the title of a 1995 period drama, adapted by Emma Thompson from a Jane Austen novel of the same name, in which Thompson appeared alongside Kate Winslet:

IDEALESS NINNY IS BEST (5, 3, 11)

7 Which actress won an Academy Award for her role in *Shakespeare in Love*, whose final line in the movie appears to be an instruction to Shakespeare to create his comedy *Twelfth Night*?

From the Classics
ANSWERS

1 The 1999 romantic comedy *10 Things I Hate About You*, starring Julia Stiles, is based on which Shakespeare play?

The Taming of the Shrew

> *10 Things I Hate About You's modernized version of the play takes place in Padua High School, in a nod to the original setting of the 16th-century comedy. Several of the characters' names are also carried over from the Shakespeare play, including the protagonist "Kat".*

2 What is the name of the 1992 animated film, which stars Matthew Broderick in a voice role, whose plot is widely considered to be based on *Hamlet*?

The Lion King

3 Which two actors appeared as the titular star-crossed lovers in the 1996 adaptation of *Romeo and Juliet*, directed and co-written by Baz Luhrmann?

Leonardo DiCaprio and Clare Danes

4 Which 1995 comedy starring Alicia Silverstone is a modern-day adaptation of Jane Austen's *Emma*?

Clueless

5 Which actor, named after the Minnesota town in which she was born, starred as Jo in the 1994 adaptation of Louisa May Alcott's *Little Women*?

Winona Ryder

6 Rearrange the letters below to reveal the title of a 1995 period drama, adapted by Emma Thompson from a Jane Austen novel of the same name, in which Thompson appeared alongside Kate Winslet:

IDEALESS NINNY IS BEST
(5, 3, 11)

Sense and Sensibility

7 Which actress won an Academy Award for her role in *Shakespeare in Love*, whose final line in the movie appears to be an instruction to Shakespeare to create his comedy *Twelfth Night*?

Judi Dench

Toy Story Movies
QUESTIONS

1. Which actor voiced the role of Hamm in *Toy Story*, marking the first of 22 consecutive appearances for the actor in Pixar feature films?

2. What is the name of the prospector character Woody encounters in *Toy Story 2*, voiced by Kelsey Grammer?

3. Change one letter in each word to restore a line spoken by Tom Hanks's character Woody when his string is pulled:

   WHERE'S I SNARE ON BY BOAT

4. In which fictional store is Woody held hostage as part of a collectors set in *Toy Story 2*, whose owner is first shown in *Toy Story* dressed in a chicken costume?

5. What is the alliterative name of the family restaurant whose truck Buzz Lightyear and Woody hang on to in the 1995 film and whose merchandising features a space theme?

6. What is the title of the song that plays in *Toy Story 2* as Jessie's abandonment is revealed, which won its creator Randy Newman a Grammy Award?

7. What is the title of the theme song written and performed by Randy Newman that appears in the opening credits for *Toy Story*, and all three of its sequel movies?

1 Which actor voiced the role of Hamm in *Toy Story*, marking the first of 22 consecutive appearances for the actor in Pixar feature films?

John Ratzenberger

Alongside his role in the Toy Story tales, Ratzenberger also appeared as The Underminer in The Incredibles, *Mack in* Cars *and the Abominable Snowman in* Monsters, Inc. *Prior to his Pixar collaborations, the actor was best known for his role as mailman Cliff Clavin in the long-running sitcom* Cheers.

2 What is the name of the prospector character Woody encounters in *Toy Story 2*, voiced by Kelsey Grammer?

Stinky Pete

3 Change one letter in each word to restore a line spoken by Tom Hanks's character Woody when his string is pulled:

WHERE'S I SNARE ON BY BOAT

"There's a snake in my boot"

4 In which fictional store is Woody held hostage as part of a collectors set in *Toy Story 2*, whose owner is first shown in *Toy Story* dressed in a chicken costume?

Al's Toy Barn

5 What is the alliterative name of the family restaurant whose truck Buzz Lightyear and Woody hang on to in the 1995 film and whose merchandising features a space theme?

Pizza Planet

6 What is the title of the song which plays in *Toy Story 2* as Jessie's abandonment is revealed, that won its creator Randy Newman a Grammy Award?

When She Loved Me

7 What is the title of the theme song written and performed by Randy Newman that appears in the opening credits for *Toy Story*, and all three of its sequel movies?

You've Got a Friend in Me

Disney 1
QUESTIONS

1 In which animated 1991 film is the song *Be Our Guest* performed by anthropomorphic household objects?

2 What was the name of the straight-to-video sequel to *Aladdin*, whose title featured the name of the original film's main antagonist?

3 Which actor and comedian, known for his roles in *Jumanji* and *Mrs. Doubtfire*, voiced the character of the Genie in 1992's *Aladdin*?

4 What kind of tree does the lead character Pocahontas receive wisdom from in the 1995 film of the same name?

5 What is the name of Simba's father in the 1994 film, *The Lion King*?

6 What is the name of Disney's first ever animated feature film which functioned as a sequel, and was released in 1990 and set in the Australian outback?

7 Which 1999 animated film features a soundtrack with songs composed and performed by Phil Collins, including the Academy-Award-winning *You'll Be in My Heart*?

1 In which animated 1991 film is the song *Be Our Guest* performed by anthropomorphic household objects?

Beauty and the Beast

The film was not originally intended to be a musical but the direction was changed after the studio's success with The Little Mermaid *in 1989, marking the start of the Walt Disney Studios "renaissance" period. Written by Alan Menken and Howard Ashman, the song was performed live at the 1992 Academy Awards—where the film's title song won Best Original Song.*

2 What was the name of the straight-to-video sequel to *Aladdin*, whose title featured the name of the original film's main antagonist?

The Return of Jafar

3 Which actor and comedian, known for his roles in *Jumanji* and *Mrs. Doubtfire*, voiced the character of the Genie in 1992's *Aladdin*?

Robin Williams

4 What kind of tree does the lead character Pocahontas receive wisdom from in the 1995 film of the same name?

Willow

5 What is the name of Simba's father in the 1994 film, *The Lion King*?

Mufasa

6 What is the name of Disney's first ever animated feature film which functioned as a sequel, and was released in 1990 and set in the Australian outback?

The Rescuers Down Under

7 Which 1999 animated film features a soundtrack with songs composed and performed by Phil Collins, including the Academy-Award-winning *You'll Be in My Heart*?

Tarzan

Quentin Tarantino
QUESTIONS

1 What is the name of the character played by Tarantino in the 1992 heist movie *Reservoir Dogs*, which he also directed?

2 Which two actors dance to the Chuck Berry song *You Can Never Tell* in *Pulp Fiction*?

3 Which one of the five 1990s movies written by Tarantino won the Academy Award for Best Original Screenplay?

4 Delete one letter in each pair below to reveal the title of a 1993 film directed by Tarantino and starring Patricia Arquette:

TP PR UL PE
FR IO MC AT ON IC EN

5 Which actor played the role of Jules Winnfield in *Pulp Fiction*, earning Academy Award and Golden Globe nominations plus also winning a BAFTA for his performance?

6 What is the title of the 1984 song by Madonna which is discussed at length in the opening scenes of *Reservoir Dogs*?

7 Pam Grier stars as which flight-attendant character in a 1997 film of the same name directed by Tarantino, opposite Samuel L. Jackson?

Quentin Tarantino
ANSWERS

1 What is the name of the character played by Tarantino in the 1992 heist movie *Reservoir Dogs*, which he also directed?

Mr. Brown

The film stars some of the actors which would come to be seen as part of Tarantino's informal "repertory" cast— including Tarantino himself, who has appeared in his own movies several times. Most of the Reservoir Dogs characters are known by color-themed names, such as "Mr. Pink" or "Mr. Blonde".

2 Which two actors dance to the Chuck Berry song *You Can Never Tell* in *Pulp Fiction*?

John Travolta and Uma Thurman

3 Which one of the five 1990s movies written by Tarantino won the Academy Award for Best Original Screenplay?

Pulp Fiction

4 Delete one letter in each pair below to reveal the title of a 1993 film directed by Tarantino and starring Patricia Arquette:

TP PR UL PE
FR IO MC AT ON IC EN

True Romance

5 Which actor played the role of Jules Winnfield in *Pulp Fiction*, earning Academy Award and Golden Globe nominations plus also winning a BAFTA for his performance?

Samuel L. Jackson

6 What is the title of the 1984 song by Madonna which is discussed at length in the opening scenes of *Reservoir Dogs*?

Like a Virgin

7 Pam Grier stars as which flight-attendant character in a 1997 film of the same name directed by Tarantino, opposite Samuel L. Jackson?

Jackie Brown

Romcoms 1
QUESTIONS

1 What is the name of the independent bookstore owned by Meg Ryan's character in the 1998 comedy drama, *You've Got Mail*?

2 On which famous Beverly Hills street is Julia Roberts's *Pretty Woman* character, Vivian, turned away from several high-end clothing stores, only to return later to declare the saleswomen's decision a "big mistake"?

3 In the movie *Sliding Doors*, Gwyneth Paltrow's character splits into two timelines —one where she boards a train and one where she misses it—in which European city?

4 Which London suburb lends it name to the title of a 1999 film, starring Hugh Grant and Julia Roberts as a bookshop owner and famous actress who fall in love?

5 Which actor played the role of Carrie in *Four Weddings and a Funeral*, delivering the iconic line "Is it raining? I hadn't noticed" in the film's romantic climax?

6 Rearrange the letters below to restore the title of a 1993 comedy drama directed by Nora Ephron:

TENSE STALE ELLIPSES (9, 2, 7)

7 Which 1995 film set in Chicago stars Sandra Bullock as a lonely ticket collector, who accidentally finds herself engaged to a man in a coma?

1 What is the name of the independent bookstore owned by Meg Ryan's character in the 1998 comedy drama, *You've Got Mail*?

The Shop Around the Corner

> *The store's title is taken from a 1940 film with the same name, which in turn was adapted into a musical film starring Judy Garland. The Shop Around the Corner and You've Got Mail were both inspired by a Hungarian play titled Parfumerie, written by Miklós László.*

2 On which famous Beverly Hills street is Julia Roberts's *Pretty Woman* character, Vivian, turned away from several high-end clothing stores, only to return later to declare the saleswomen's decision a "big mistake"?

Rodeo Drive

3 In the movie *Sliding Doors*, Gwyneth Paltrow's character splits into two timelines—one where she boards a train and one where she misses it—in which European city?

London

4 Which London suburb lends it name to the title of a 1999 film, starring Hugh Grant and Julia Roberts as a bookshop owner and famous actress who fall in love?

Notting Hill

5 Which actor played the role of Carrie in *Four Weddings and a Funeral*, delivering the iconic line "Is it raining? I hadn't noticed" in the film's romantic climax?

Andie MacDowell

6 Rearrange the letters below to restore the title of a 1993 comedy drama directed by Nora Ephron:

TENSE STALE ELLIPSES (9, 2, 7)

Sleepless in Seattle

7 Which 1995 film set in Chicago stars Sandra Bullock as a lonely ticket collector, who accidentally finds herself engaged to a man in a coma?

While You Were Sleeping

Prize Winners 1
QUESTIONS

1   Which prolific British playwright was portrayed by Joseph Fiennes in a 1998 film that went on to win the Academy Award for Best Picture?

2   What are the titles of the three stop-motion pictures created by Nick Park which won Academy Awards for Best Animated Short Film in the 1990s?

3   Who wrote the original novel on which the film *Babe* was based, which won Best Visual Effects at the 1996 Academy Awards?

4   Which film starring Gwyneth Paltrow, based on a book of the same name by Jane Austen, won the Academy Award for Best Original Music or Comedy Score in 1997?

5   Which British actor won the Oscar for Best Supporting Actor for his role in *The Cider House Rules*, 13 years after he won the same award for the Woody Allen film *Hannah and Her Sisters*?

6   In what language was *Life Is Beautiful* written and filmed, later winning several Academy Awards and the Grand Prix at the 1998 Cannes Film Festival?

7   Who won the Oscar for Best Director for the 1990 Western film *Dancing with Wolves*, in which he also starred, and which was also his directorial debut?

Prize Winners 1

ANSWERS

1 Which prolific British playwright was portrayed by Joseph Fiennes in a 1998 film that went on to win the Academy Award for Best Picture?

William Shakespeare

Shakespeare in Love also starred Gwyneth Paltrow and Judi Dench, who won Oscars for their lead and supporting roles, respectively. The movie was one of the top-ten highest grossing movies of 1998, and featured many elements that allude to Shakespeare's plays.

2 What are the titles of the three stop-motion pictures created by Nick Park which won Academy Awards for Best Animated Short Film in the 1990s?

***Creature Comforts* in 1990, *The Wrong Trousers* in 1993, and *A Close Shave* in 1995**

3 Who wrote the original novel on which the film *Babe* was based, which won Best Visual Effects at the 1996 Academy Awards?

Dick King-Smith

4 Which film starring Gwyneth Paltrow, based on a book of the same name by Jane Austen, won the Academy Award for Best Original Music or Comedy Score in 1997?

Emma

5 Which British actor won the Oscar for Best Supporting Actor for his role in *The Cider House Rules*, 13 years after he won the same award for the Woody Allen film *Hannah and Her Sisters*?

Michael Caine

6 In what language was *Life Is Beautiful* written and filmed, later winning several Academy Awards and the Grand Prix at the 1998 Cannes Film Festival?

Italian

7 Who won the Oscar for Best Director for the 1990 Western film *Dancing with Wolves*, in which he also starred, and which was also his directorial debut?

Kevin Costner

Sci-Fi 1
QUESTIONS

1 Which 1990 film starred Arnold Schwarzenegger as a construction worker who has false memories of a trip to Mars implanted in his mind?

2 In *Men in Black*, what are the names of the two main protagonists, played by Tommy Lee Jones and Will Smith?

3 Which actor and director played the role of Jurassic Park creator John Hammond in the 1993 blockbuster movie?

4 What animal is seen on the jewelry of Vivica A. Fox's character Jasmine in 1996's *Independence Day*, sparking an uptick in sales for items featuring the same aquatic mammal?

5 Rearrange the letters below to restore the name of a 1997 film starring Bruce Willis and Gary Oldman, set in the 23rd century:

FINE HELMET THEFT
(3, 5, 7)

6 In how many feature films released during the 1990s did Patrick Stewart star as Jean-Luc Picard, captain of the star ship *Enterprise*?

7 Which 1998 film with the tagline "Fight The Future" was a follow-up to a TV series featuring the characters Mulder and Scully?

1 Which 1990 film starred Arnold Schwarzenegger as a construction worker who has false memories of a trip to Mars implanted in his mind?

Total Recall

> *The film is based on a 1966 short story* We Can Remember It for You Wholesale, *written by Philip K. Dick, whose works also inspired the films* Blade Runner *and* Minority Report. *The story was later reused in a 2012 film, also called* Total Recall, *starring Colin Farrell.*

2 In *Men in Black*, what are the names of the two main protagonists, played by Tommy Lee Jones and Will Smith?

Agent K and Agent D, respectively

3 Which actor and director played the role of Jurassic Park creator John Hammond in the 1993 blockbuster movie?

Richard Attenborough

4 What animal is seen on the jewelry of Vivica A. Fox's character Jasmine in 1996's *Independence Day*, sparking an uptick in sales for items featuring the same aquatic mammal?

Dolphin

5 Rearrange the letters below to restore the name of a 1997 film starring Bruce Willis and Gary Oldman, set in the 23rd century:

FINE HELMET THEFT (3, 5, 7)

The Fifth Element

6 In how many feature films released during the 1990s did Patrick Stewart star as Jean-Luc Picard, captain of the star ship *Enterprise*?

Three: *Star Trek Generations*, *Star Trek: First Contact* and *Star Trek: Insurrection*

7 Which 1998 film with the tagline "Fight The Future" was a follow-up to a TV series featuring the characters Mulder and Scully?

The X-Files

Festive Films
QUESTIONS

1 Which actress both voiced the role of Sally in *The Nightmare Before Christmas* and played the protagonist's mother in *Home Alone*?

2 What is the title of the 1994 comedy starring Tim Allen as a man who accidentally injures an iconic festive figure on Christmas Eve, then finds himself legally obliged to complete that man's unfinished festive tasks?

3 Rearrange the letters below to reveal the name of the actor who plays Kris Kringle —later determined to be the real Santa Claus—in the 1994 film *Miracle on 34th Street*:

HURRAH ACTING OR TO BED (7, 12)

4 Which role, present in Charles Dickens's original story, does Michael Caine play in *The Muppet Christmas Carol*?

5 Starring Arnold Schwarzenegger and Sinbad as two feuding fathers desperately searching for a toy for their children, which 1996 comedy was inspired by "the Cabbage Patch Kid riots"?

6 In which US city does the sequel to *Home Alone* take place?

7 In the 1990 comedy *Home Alone*, which European capital city do Kevin's family fly to without him?

1 Which actress both voiced the role of Sally in *The Nightmare Before Christmas* and played the protagonist's mother in *Home Alone*?

Catherine O'Hara

> *In* Home Alone *and its sequel, Kevin's mother is the one who realizes—too late—that her son has not joined them on the family trip. In* The Nightmare Before Christmas, *O'Hara is the voice—both spoken and sung—of Sally, the toxicologist love interest of the film's protagonist, Jack Skellington.*

2 What is the title of the 1994 comedy starring Tim Allen as a man who accidentally injures an iconic festive figure on Christmas Eve, then finds himself legally obliged to complete that man's unfinished festive tasks?

The Santa Clause

3 Rearrange the letters below to reveal the name of the actor who plays Kris Kringle—later determined to be the real Santa Claus—in the 1994 film *Miracle on 34th Street*:

HURRAH ACTING OR TO BED (7, 12)

Richard Attenborough

4 Which role, present in Charles Dickens's original story, does Michael Caine play in *The Muppet Christmas Carol*?

Ebenezer Scrooge

5 Starring Arnold Schwarzenegger and Sinbad as two feuding fathers desperately searching for a toy for their children, which 1996 comedy was inspired by "the Cabbage Patch Kid riots"?

Jingle All the Way

6 In which US city does the sequel to *Home Alone* take place?

New York City

7 In the 1990 comedy *Home Alone*, which European capital city do Kevin's family fly to without him?

Paris

Jim Carrey
QUESTIONS

1 In a 1994 film starring Carrey and Cameron Diaz, what color is the mask that gives the movie its title?

2 In which 1997 fantasy film does Carrey star as a lawyer who is forced to tell the truth for one day, after his son makes a birthday wish to that effect?

3 What is the name of the "pet detective" played by Carrey in two films from the 1990s, who is tasked with the capture of various domesticated animals?

4 What antagonist role did Carrey play in 1995's *Batman Forever*, costumed in a lime green unitard emblazoned with question marks?

5 Which comedian and actor, considered to be a member of the comedy "Frat Pack", directed *The Cable Guy*, starring Carrey and Matthew Broderick?

6 Change one letter in each word below to reveal the title of a 1999 biographical film which starred Carrey as entertainer Andy Kaufman:

MAY IN TOE MOAN

7 What is the name of the fictional town created within *The Truman Show*, in which the eponymous Truman is filmed throughout every day of his life?

1 In a 1994 film starring Carrey and Cameron Diaz, what color is the mask that gives the movie its title?

Green

Capable of giving its wearers apparently unlimited power, while seemingly robbing them of their sanity, the green mask transforms Jim Carrey's character into a capricious shape-shifting figure. The film is an adaptation of the The Mask comics, which in turn drew some inspiration from the characters of Dr. Jekyll and Mr. Hyde.

2 In which 1997 fantasy film does Carrey star as a lawyer who is forced to tell the truth for one day, after his son makes a birthday wish to that effect?

Liar Liar

3 What is the name of the "pet detective" played by Carrey in two films from the 1990s, who is tasked with the capture of various domesticated animals?

Ace Ventura

4 What antagonist role did Carrey play in 1995's *Batman Forever*, costumed in a lime green unitard emblazoned with question marks?

The Riddler

5 Which comedian and actor, considered to be a member of the comedy "Frat Pack", directed *The Cable Guy*, starring Carrey and Matthew Broderick?

Ben Stiller

6 Change one letter in each word below to reveal the title of a 1999 biographical film which starred Carrey as entertainer Andy Kaufman:

MAY IN TOE MOAN

Man on the Moon

7 What is the name of the fictional town created within *The Truman Show*, in which the eponymous Truman is filmed throughout every day of his life?

Seahaven Island

Taglines
QUESTIONS

Can you name the movies which were promoted with each of the following taglines when they were released in the 1990s?

1 "A lot can happen in the middle of nowhere."

2 "Mischief. Mayhem. Soap."

3 "How do I loathe thee? Let me count the ways."

4 "On the air. Unaware."

5 "The mission is a man."

6 "His story will touch you, even though he can't."

7 "One Dream. Four Jamaicans. Twenty below zero."

8 "He's in town with a few days to kill."

9 "A story about love at second sight."

10 "They've saved the best trip for last... But this time they may have gone too far."

11 "You know the name. You know the number."

Can you name the movies which were promoted with each of the following taglines when they were released in the 1990s?

1 "A lot can happen in the middle of nowhere."

Fargo

Released in 1996 and directed by the Coen brothers, Fargo takes its name from that of a real city in North Dakota. Despite this, none of the filming took place in the real Fargo, and most of the action takes place in the neighboring state of Minnesota.

2 "Mischief. Mayhem. Soap."

Fight Club

3 "How do I loathe thee? Let me count the ways."

10 Things I Hate About You

4 "On the air. Unaware."

The Truman Show

5 "The mission is a man."

Saving Private Ryan

6 "His story will touch you, even though he can't."

Edward Scissorhands

7 "One Dream. Four Jamaicans. Twenty below zero."

Cool Runnings

8 "He's in town with a few days to kill."

Predator 2

9 "A story about love at second sight."

While You Were Sleeping

10 "They've saved the best trip for last... But this time they may have gone too far."

Back to the Future III

11 "You know the name. You know the number."

GoldenEye

Supernatural
QUESTIONS

1 In which supernatural thriller is the iconic line "I see dead people" spoken by Haley Joel Osment's character?

2 Change one letter in each word below to reveal the name of a 1999 horror film set in an abandoned asylum, starring Geoffrey Rush and Taye Diggs:

MOUSE IN TAUNTED JILL

3 In which gothic 1999 horror film does Johnny Depp star as Ichabod Crane, a police constable sent to investigate grisly murders in the rural town which gives the movie its name?

4 Which 1999 "found footage" horror film shows the audience video material supposedly captured by the three protagonists as they investigate a local supernatural legend?

5 Which actor plays the title role in the 1992 film *Bram Stoker's Dracula*, directed by Francis Ford Coppola and also starring Winona Ryder and Anthony Hopkins?

6 Who directed all three of *Sleepy Hollow*, *Mars Attacks!*, and *Edward Scissorhands*?

7 What is the name of the titular high priest accidentally awoken in 1999's *The Mummy*, starring Brendan Fraser and Rachel Weisz?

1 In which supernatural thriller is the iconic line "I see dead people" spoken by Haley Joel Osment's character?

The Sixth Sense

Released in 1999 and starring Bruce Willis in a titular role, the movie boasts perhaps one of the most iconic twists in cinematic history. The Sixth Sense was written and directed by M. Night Shyamalan, earning him Academy Award nominations for Best Director and Best Original Screenplay.

2 Change one letter in each word below to reveal the name of a 1999 horror film set in an abandoned asylum, starring Geoffrey Rush and Taye Diggs:

MOUSE IN TAUNTED JILL

House on Haunted Hill

3 In which gothic 1999 horror film does Johnny Depp star as Ichabod Crane, a police constable sent to investigate grisly murders in the rural town which gives the movie its name?

Sleepy Hollow

4 Which 1999 "found footage" horror film shows the audience video material supposedly captured by the three protagonists as they investigate a local supernatural legend?

The Blair Witch Project

5 Which actor plays the title role in the 1992 film *Bram Stoker's Dracula*, directed by Francis Ford Coppola and also starring Winona Ryder and Anthony Hopkins?

Gary Oldman

6 Who directed all three of *Sleepy Hollow*, *Mars Attacks!*, and *Edward Scissorhands*?

Tim Burton

7 What is the name of the titular high priest accidentally awoken in 1999's *The Mummy*, starring Brendan Fraser and Rachel Weisz?

Imhotep

Denzel Washington
QUESTIONS

1. Which 1993 legal drama, which takes its name from a US city, stars Washington as an attorney who takes on the wrongful dismissal case of Tom Hanks's character Andrew Beckett?

2. Rearrange the letters below to reveal the title of a 1999 biographical sports drama starring Washington as boxer Rubin Carter:

   HURTER IN EACH (3, 9)

3. Which 1993 legal thriller stars Washington and Julia Roberts as a journalist and lawyer, trying to uncover a conspiracy which would endanger a seabird found in the film's title?

4. Which civil rights activist did Washington portray in an eponymous 1992 biographical drama directed by Spike Lee, winning him an Academy Award nomination for Best Actor?

5. Which singer and actor, often nicknamed "The Voice", starred as the titular character who falls in love with an angel, played by Washington, in the 1996 comedy drama *The Preacher's Wife*?

6. Change one letter in each word below to restore the title of a 1990 comedy drama starring Washington that was written, produced and directed by Spike Lee:

   MY' BATTER CLUES

7. In which 1993 adaptation of a Shakespeare play of the same name did Washington star alongside Kenneth Branagh, who also served as adaptor and director?

Denzel Washington

ANSWERS

1 Which 1993 legal drama, which takes its name from a US city, stars Washington as an attorney who takes on the wrongful dismissal case of Tom Hanks's character Andrew Beckett?

Philadelphia

> *The film was nominated for several prestigious awards, and was notable at the time for being one of the first major movies to address the AIDS epidemic. Tom Hanks went on the win the Academy Award for Best Actor for his role.*

2 Rearrange the letters below to reveal the title of a 1999 biographical sports drama starring Washington as boxer Rubin Carter:

HURTER IN EACH (3, 9)

The Hurricane

3 Which 1993 legal thriller stars Washington and Julia Roberts as a journalist and lawyer, trying to uncover a conspiracy which would endanger a seabird found in the film's title?

The Pelican Brief

4 Which civil rights activist did Washington portray in the eponymous 1992 biographical drama directed by Spike Lee, for which he earned an Academy Award nomination for Best Actor?

Malcolm X

5 Which singer and actor, often nicknamed "The Voice", starred as the titular character who falls in love with an angel, played by Washington, in the 1996 comedy drama *The Preacher's Wife*?

Whitney Houston

6 Change one letter in each word below to restore the title of a 1990 comedy drama starring Washington that was written, produced and directed by Spike Lee:

MY' BATTER CLUES

Mo' Better Blues

7 In which 1993 adaptation of a Shakespeare play of the same name did Washington star alongside Kenneth Branagh, who also served as adaptor and director?

Much Ado About Nothing

Romantic Thrillers
QUESTIONS

1 What is the title of the song which plays over the iconic "pottery scene" in the 1990 thriller, *Ghost*?

2 After saying her goodbyes to Kevin Costner's character at the end of *The Bodyguard*, which song written by Dolly Parton is Whitney Houston shown singing?

3 In the neo-noir thriller *Basic Instinct*, which actor stars as a serial killer whose killings mimic those created for the character's own crime novels?

4 Which actress played the role of psychic medium Oda Mae Brown in *Ghost*, winning an Academy Award for Best Supporting Actress for her performance?

5 Which member of Spandau Ballet makes an appearance in *The Bodyguard* as Sy Spector, PR assistant to Whitney Houston's character Rachel?

6 Rearrange the letters below to reveal the title of a 1999 film starring Reese Witherspoon, which is an adaptation of the French novel *Les Liaisons Dangereuses*:

INNOCENTER I LUST
(5, 10)

7 Which Shakespeare play, opening with the appearance of a ghost, did *Ghost* writer Bruce Joel Rubin say was the initial inspiration behind creating his screenplay?

Romantic Thrillers
ANSWERS

1 What is the title of the song which plays over the iconic "pottery scene" in the 1990 thriller, *Ghost*?

Unchained Melody

The scene opens with a jukebox-style music player setting up the track as Demi Moore's character crafts a tall, elegant vase. Occurring before Patrick Swayze's shirtless character becomes the titular ghost, the scene is one of the most iconic—and parodied—in modern cinema.

2 After saying her goodbyes to Kevin Costner's character at the end of *The Bodyguard*, which song written by Dolly Parton is Whitney Houston shown singing?

I Will Always Love You

3 In the neo-noir thriller *Basic Instinct*, which actor stars as a serial killer whose killings mimic those created for the character's own crime novels?

Sharon Stone

4 Which actress played the role of psychic medium Oda Mae Brown in *Ghost*, winning an Academy Award for Best Supporting Actress for her performance?

Whoopi Goldberg

5 Which member of Spandau Ballet makes an appearance in *The Bodyguard* as Sy Spector, PR assistant to Whitney Houston's character Rachel?

Gary Kemp

6 Rearrange the letters below to reveal the title of a 1999 film starring Reese Witherspoon, which is an adaptation of the French novel *Les Liaisons Dangereuses*:

INNOCENTER I LUST (5, 10)

Cruel Intentions

7 Which Shakespeare play, opening with the appearance of a ghost, did *Ghost* writer Bruce Joel Rubin say was the initial inspiration behind creating his screenplay?

Hamlet

Disney 2
QUESTIONS

1. Which song, written by Tim Rice and Elton John, won the Academy Award for Best Original Song after featuring in *The Lion King*?

2. Which Walt Disney Studios stop-motion animation film, produced by Tim Burton in 1993, marked a contrast with Disney's previous animated feature films?

3. Which prestigious musical award did the *Aladdin* song *A Whole New World* win in 1994, becoming the first song from a Disney feature to win in that category?

4. Which 1997 film title can be given in answer to the question, "Who puts the glad in gladiator?", according to one of that movie's musical numbers?

5. What is the name of the anthropomorphic dragon sidekick, voiced by Eddie Murphy, in the 1998 musical film *Mulan*?

6. Which British actor and comedian voiced the role of the hornbill Zazu in *The Lion King*?

7. In which city is *The Hunchback of Notre Dame* set?

1 Which song, written by Tim Rice and Elton John, won the Academy Award for Best Original Song after featuring in *The Lion King*?

Can You Feel the Love Tonight

For his performance in a version played over the closing credits, Elton John won the Grammy for Best Male Pop Vocal Performance. The song performed well as a commercial single, reaching number one in both Canada and France in 1994, and features backing vocals from British musicians Rick Astley and Gary Barlow.

2 Which Walt Disney Studios stop-motion animation film, produced by Tim Burton in 1993, marked a contrast with Disney's previous animated feature films?

The Nightmare Before Christmas

3 Which prestigious musical award did the *Aladdin* song *A Whole New World* win in 1994, becoming the first song from a Disney feature to win in that category?

Grammy Award for Song of the Year

4 Which 1997 film title can be given in answer to the question, "Who puts the glad in gladiator?", according to one of that movie's musical numbers?

Hercules

5 What is the name of the anthropomorphic dragon sidekick, voiced by Eddie Murphy, in the 1998 musical film *Mulan*?

Mushu

6 Which British actor and comedian voiced the role of the hornbill Zazu in *The Lion King*?

Rowan Atkinson

7 In which city is *The Hunchback of Notre Dame* set?

Paris

Pot Luck
QUESTIONS

1. Which Australian comedy-drama, released in 1994, stars Toni Collette as the titular character who is desperate to escape from her home town of Porpoise Spit?

2. What is the name of the spy played by Tom Cruise in the 1996 action film *Mission: Impossible*, as well as its later sequels?

3. Change one letter in each word below to reveal the title of a 1996 film written and directed by Tom Hanks, in which he also starred:

   WHAT TYING YOB SO

4. Which 1996 slasher movie features an ensemble cast facing an unknown masked assailant who becomes known as "Ghostface"?

5. Which actor starred as the titular character in 1998's *The Mask of Zorro*, opposite Catherine Zeta-Jones?

6. Which 1990 film directed by Martin Scorsese, and starring Robert De Niro, is a biographical drama focusing on the true crimes of Henry Hill and his associates?

7. In the 1995 docudrama *Apollo 13*, which household appliance does the protagonist's mother comment that her son would be able to land, if anyone were able to make it fly?

1. Which Australian comedy-drama, released in 1994, stars Toni Collette as the titular character who is desperate to escape from her home town of Porpoise Spit?

Muriel's Wedding

> *Directed by P. J. Hogan,* Muriel's Wedding *follows the ups and downs of one woman's life in a seemingly depressing beach town. The music of ABBA, being the favorite band of the eponymous Muriel, features heavily in the film's soundtrack—including an orchestral arrangement of the 1975 hit* Dancing Queen.

2. What is the name of the spy played by Tom Cruise in the 1996 action film *Mission: Impossible*, as well as its later sequels?

Ethan Hunt

3. Change one letter in each word below to reveal the title of a 1996 film written and directed by Tom Hanks, in which he also starred:

WHAT TYING YOB SO

That Thing You Do

4. Which 1996 slasher movie features an ensemble cast facing an unknown masked assailant who becomes known as "Ghostface"?

Scream

5. Which actor starred as the titular character in 1998's *The Mask of Zorro*, opposite Catherine Zeta-Jones?

Antonio Banderas

6. Which 1990 film directed by Martin Scorsese, and starring Robert De Niro, is a biographical drama focusing on the true crimes of Henry Hill and his associates?

Goodfellas

7. In the 1995 docudrama *Apollo 13*, which household appliance does the protagonist's mother comment that her son would be able to land, if anyone were able to make it fly?

A washing machine

Spielberg Movies
QUESTIONS

1. When the group initially arrive in *Jurassic Park*, what is the first species of dinosaur they see?

2. For which 1997 film did actors Will Smith and Tommy Lee Jones only accept their roles after hearing that Steven Spielberg was attached as an executive producer?

3. Rearrange the letters below to spell out the name of Dr. Ian Malcolm's mathematical specialty in both *Jurassic Park* and its sequel, in a role played by Jeff Goldblum:

   CHOOSY EARTH (5, 6)

4. What is the codename given to the Normandy beach on which the action in *Saving Private Ryan* opens, sharing its name with a city in Nebraska?

5. What is the title of Spielberg's 1997 historical drama film set on board a Spanish slave ship, which translates into English as "friendship"?

6. Which Oscar-winning actress played the role of Tinker Bell in the 1991 film *Hook*?

7. Which composer and long-time collaborator with Spielberg wrote the Oscar-winning score for *Schindler's List*?

Spielberg Movies
ANSWERS

1 When the group initially arrive in *Jurassic Park*, what is the first species of dinosaur they see?

Brachiosaurus

> After emerging shell-shocked from the Jeep which brings the visitors to the compound, Sam Neill's character points to the long-necked herbivore and exclaims, "It's a dinosaur". The film was shot in Hawaii, although production was delayed at one point when caught in the direct path of a hurricane—and so some of the storm sequences are real footage of the weather during shooting.

2 For which 1997 film did actors Will Smith and Tommy Lee Jones only accept their roles after hearing that Steven Spielberg was attached as an executive producer?

Men in Black

3 Rearrange the letters below to spell out the name of Dr. Ian Malcolm's mathematical specialty in both *Jurassic Park* and its sequel, in a role played by Jeff Goldblum:

CHOOSY EARTH (5, 6)

Chaos Theory

4 What is the codename given to the Normandy beach on which the action in *Saving Private Ryan* opens, sharing its name with a city in Nebraska?

Omaha

5 What is the title of Spielberg's 1997 historical drama film set on board a Spanish slave ship, which translates into English as "friendship"?

Amistad

6 Which Oscar-winning actress played the role of Tinker Bell in the 1991 film *Hook*?

Julia Roberts

7 Which composer and long-time collaborator with Spielberg wrote the Oscar-winning score for *Schindler's List*?

John Williams

Sci-Fi 2
QUESTIONS

1 Which 1998 disaster film, starring Bruce Willis and Liv Tyler as father and daughter, featured the song *I Don't Want to Miss a Thing*, sung by Liv's real-life father Steven Tyler?

2 Which is the only film in the *Star Wars* franchise that was first released during the 1990s?

3 What is the name of Carrie-Anne Moss's character in the 1999 sci-fi action film, *The Matrix*?

4 Which 1991 sequel movie, directed by James Cameron, starred Linda Hamilton in the role of Sarah Connor as well as her twin sister as an android who imitates her?

5 Delete one letter in each pair to reveal the name of a 1999 sci-fi comedy starring Sigourney Weaver and Alan Rickman, notable for its gentle satire of the *Star Trek* franchise and its fans:

GS PA CL AE QX WY DQ UR AE SM TA

6 Who directed *Mars Attacks!*, a film featuring computer-animated aliens based on the Topps trading cards, which was originally planned to be filmed with stop-motion creatures?

7 What is the nickname of the robot played by Robin Williams in the 1999 comedy-drama *Bicentennial Man*, directed by Chris Columbus?

1 Which 1998 disaster film, starring Bruce Willis and Liv Tyler as father and daughter, featured the song *I Don't Want to Miss a Thing*, sung by Liv's real-life father Steven Tyler?

Armageddon

The song was performed by the band Aerosmith, and went on to become the band's first US number one. The band performed four songs overall for the movie, including Sweet Emotion *and* Come Together, *the latter of which had previously been a hit for The Beatles.*

2 Which is the only film in the *Star Wars* franchise that was first released during the 1990s?

Episode I: The Phantom Menace

3 What is the name of Carrie-Anne Moss's character in the 1999 sci-fi action film, *The Matrix*?

Trinity

4 Which 1991 sequel movie, directed by James Cameron, starred Linda Hamilton in the role of Sarah Connor as well as her twin sister as an android who imitates her?

Terminator 2: Judgment Day

5 Delete one letter in each pair to reveal the name of a 1999 sci-fi comedy starring Sigourney Weaver and Alan Rickman, notable for its gentle satire of the *Star Trek* franchise and its fans:

GS PA CL AE QX WY
DQ UR AE SM TA

Galaxy Quest

6 Who directed *Mars Attacks!*, a film featuring computer-animated aliens based on the Topps trading cards, which was originally planned to be filmed with stop-motion creatures?

Tim Burton

7 What is the nickname of the robot played by Robin Williams in the 1999 comedy-drama *Bicentennial Man*, directed by Chris Columbus?

Andrew

Comedies
QUESTIONS

1 In *Groundhog Day*, what Sonny & Cher song plays on the radio alarm clock each morning, as Bill Murray's character wakes up to find that each day is the same as the last?

2 Which character, created by *Saturday Night Live* alumnus Mike Myers, was the protagonist of a 1997 film that was a comic pastiche of the *James Bond* franchise?

3 Which 1997 comedy, co-written by Richard Curtis, stars Rowan Atkinson as a hapless security guard who must pretend to be an art expert on a trip abroad?

4 Which actor played the titular role in the 1998 comedy *There's Something About Mary*, which also starred comedian Ben Stiller?

5 What are the first names of the two protagonists in the 1994 screwball comedy *Dumb and Dumber*, played by Jeff Daniels and Jim Carrey?

6 Rearrange the letters below to reveal the name of a comedy starring Adam Sandler and Drew Barrymore, released in 1998 but set in the 1980s:

WHINGING, DESERTED (3, 7, 6)

7 What is the title of the 1992 comedy which stars Wesley Snipes and Woody Harrelson as a basketball-playing duo who use their skills on the court to swindle other players out of money?

Comedies
ANSWERS

1 In *Groundhog Day*, what Sonny & Cher song plays on the radio alarm clock each morning, as Bill Murray's character wakes up to find that each day is the same as the last?

I Got You Babe

At 06:00 every day, for what seems to him like an eternity, Bill Murray's character wakes up to the 1965 classic sung by Sonny & Cher. On the very first Groundhog Day in the movie, Phil Connors appears irritated to be waking up to the song, and he becomes no more cheerful as the same wakeup call then repeats over and over again on subsequent days.

2 Which character, created by *Saturday Night Live* alumnus Mike Myers, was the protagonist of a 1997 film that was a comic pastiche of the *James Bond* franchise?

Austin Powers

3 Which 1997 comedy, co-written by Richard Curtis, stars Rowan Atkinson as a hapless security guard who must pretend to be an art expert on a trip abroad?

Bean

4 Which actor played the titular role in the 1998 comedy *There's Something About Mary*, which also starred comedian Ben Stiller?

Cameron Diaz

5 What are the first names of the two protagonists in the 1994 screwball comedy *Dumb and Dumber*, played by Jeff Daniels and Jim Carrey?

Harry and Lloyd

6 Rearrange the letters below to reveal the name of a comedy starring Adam Sandler and Drew Barrymore, released in 1998 but set in the 1980s:

WHINGING, DESERTED (3, 7, 6)

The Wedding Singer

7 What is the title of the 1992 comedy which stars Wesley Snipes and Woody Harrelson as a basketball-playing duo who use their skills on the court to swindle other players out of money?

White Men Can't Jump

Titanic
QUESTIONS

1. What is the full name of the 17-year-old character played by Kate Winslet, during her time on board the *Titanic*?

2. Change one letter in each word below to reveal the name of a song recorded by Celine Dion which famously features in the soundtrack to the film:

   BY HEARS WILT NO IN

3. What is the name of the US department store which was co-owned by Isidor Straus, who is portrayed in the movie alongside his wife as a couple who did not survive the sinking?

4. How many years passed between the sinking of the *Titanic* and the release of the Academy-Award winning film?

5. Which actor plays the role of Caledon Hockley, a wealthy heir engaged to Kate Winslet's character?

6. Who not only wrote and directed but also produced *Titanic*?

7. What is the name of the jewelled necklace thrown into the water at the end of the film?

1 What is the full name of the 17-year-old character played by Kate Winslet, during her time on board the *Titanic*?

Rose DeWitt Bukater

> *The character's first appearance in the movie—which begins non-chronologically, in 1996—is as Rose Dawson Calvert. In the following scenes set in 1912, she boards the Titanic as a 17-year-old, with her family and fiancé. Later, after the sinking, she gives her name as Rose Dawson.*

2 Change one letter in each word below to reveal the name of a song recorded by Celine Dion which famously features in the soundtrack to the film:

BY HEARS WILT NO IN

My Heart Will Go On

3 What is the name of the US department store which was co-owned by Isidor Straus, who is portrayed in the movie alongside his wife as a couple who did not survive the sinking?

Macy's

4 How many years passed between the sinking of the *Titanic* and the release of the Academy-Award winning film?

85 years, from 1912 to 1997

5 Which actor plays the role of Caledon Hockley, a wealthy heir engaged to Kate Winslet's character?

Billy Zane

6 Who not only wrote and directed but also produced *Titanic*?

James Cameron

7 What is the name of the jewelled necklace thrown into the water at the end of the film?

The Heart of the Ocean

Robin Williams
QUESTIONS

1 "Flubber", named by Robin Williams's mad-scientist character Professor Brainard in the 1997 sci-fi comedy of the same name, is a portmanteau of which two words?

2 Change one letter in each word below to reveal the name of a 1991 film starring Williams and Jeff Bridges as two men who search for a holy grail. It was directed by former Monty Python member Terry Gilliam.

SHE FISHES WING

3 Which actor starred as the titular antagonist in *Hook*, earning a Golden Globe nomination for Best Actor—which he lost to co-star Robin Williams who had been nominated for a different film?

4 Which two actors wrote the screenplay for *Good Will Hunting*, both appearing alongside Williams in a role for which he won the Academy Award for Best Supporting Actor?

5 In which 1995 adventure film does Williams play a character inadvertently sucked into a jungle-themed board game?

6 What predominant color is the genie, voiced by Williams, in the 1992 Disney animated film *Aladdin*?

7 In the 1993 movie *Mrs. Doubtfire*, what is Mrs. Doubtfire's first name?

1 "Flubber", named by Robin Williams's mad-scientist character Professor Brainard in the 1997 sci-fi comedy of the same name, is a portmanteau of which two words?

Flying rubber

> *The film is a remake of the 1961 film The Absent-Minded Professor, where the mischievous green substance was given the same name as in the 1997 title. After discovering its various anti-gravity effects, Williams's professor decides to use the newly named creation to put his life back together.*

2 Change one letter in each word below to reveal the name of a 1991 film starring Williams and Jeff Bridges as two men who search for a holy grail. It was directed by former Monty Python member Terry Gilliam.

SHE FISHES WING

The Fisher King

3 Which actor starred as the titular antagonist in *Hook*, earning a Golden Globe nomination for Best Actor—which he lost to co-star Robin Williams who had been nominated for a different film?

Dustin Hoffman

4 Which two actors wrote the screenplay for *Good Will Hunting*, both appearing alongside Williams in a role for which he won the Academy Award for Best Supporting Actor?

Matt Damon and Ben Affleck

5 In which 1995 adventure film does Williams play a character inadvertently sucked into a jungle-themed board game?

Jumanji

6 What predominant color is the genie, voiced by Williams, in the 1992 Disney animated film *Aladdin*?

Blue

7 In the 1993 movie *Mrs. Doubtfire*, what is Mrs. Doubtfire's first name?

Euphegenia

Cult Classics
QUESTIONS

1. What is the name of the character played by Frances McDormand in *Fargo*, in a performance for which she won the Academy Award for Best Actress?

2. Which 1996 film set in Edinburgh and starring Ewan McGregor was based on an Irvine Welsh novel of the same name?

3. Who wrote and directed the 1999 psychological drama *The Virgin Suicides*, starring Kirsten Dunst?

4. According to the movie's protagonists, what is the first rule of Fight Club?

5. Which 1998 crime film, created by the Coen brothers, stars Jeff Bridges as "The Dude"?

6. Which two actors star as the main protagonists in *Fear and Loathing in Las Vegas*, first seen driving across the desert in a red Chevrolet Impala?

7. Rearrange the letters below to create the title of a 1999 comedy, starring Ron Livingston and Jennifer Aniston as a pair who battle against corporate culture:

   A SCOFF PIECE (6, 5)

Cult Classics
ANSWERS

1 What is the name of the character played by Frances McDormand in *Fargo*, in a performance for which she won the Academy Award for Best Actress?

Marge Gunderson

McDormand reputedly spoke with a pregnant police officer to prepare for the role as the police chief, as well as learning how to handle firearms. Her character displays one of the film's classic examples of the stereotype "Minnesota nice", with a mild-mannered tone and courteous behavior.

2 Which 1996 film set in Edinburgh and starring Ewan McGregor was based on an Irvine Welsh novel of the same name?

Trainspotting

3 Who wrote and directed the 1999 psychological drama *The Virgin Suicides*, starring Kirsten Dunst?

Sofia Coppola

4 According to the movie's protagonists, what is the first rule of Fight Club?

"Do not talk about fight club"

5 Which 1998 crime film, created by the Coen brothers, stars Jeff Bridges as "The Dude"?

The Big Lebowski

6 Which two actors star as the main protagonists in *Fear and Loathing in Las Vegas*, first seen driving across the desert in a red Chevrolet Impala?

Johnny Depp and Benicio del Toro

7 Rearrange the letters below to create the title of a 1999 comedy, starring Ron Livingston and Jennifer Aniston as a pair who battle against corporate culture:

A SCOFF PIECE (6, 5)

Office Space

Prize Winners 2
QUESTIONS

1 Who played the role of serial killer Hannibal Lecter in the 1991 film *The Silence of the Lambs*, winning a BAFTA and an Oscar for his performance?

2 Which film won Best Picture at the 69th Academy Awards, and Best Film at the 50th BAFTA awards, plus also earned Best Actor and Best Actress nominations for Ralph Fiennes and Kristin Scott Thomas in the same ceremonies?

3 Which actor, well known for appearing in Western films, produced, directed and starred in *Unforgiven*, later winning an Oscar and a Golden Globe for his direction?

4 For which 1995 film did Mel Gibson win both an Oscar and a Golden Globe for his direction, and in which he starred as Sir William Wallace?

5 Which director won an Academy Award, Golden Globe and Director's Guild of America award for his direction of the film *American Beauty*?

6 Who wrote and directed *All About My Mother*, the 1999 Spanish-language winner of the Oscar for Best Foreign Language Film?

7 Which 1994 film won six of the thirteen Academy Awards it had been nominated for, including Best Picture?

Prize Winners 2

1 Who played the role of serial killer Hannibal Lecter in the 1991 film *The Silence of the Lambs*, winning a BAFTA and an Oscar for his performance?

Anthony Hopkins

> *Starring alongside Jodie Foster—who also won an Oscar for her performance—Hopkins later revealed that he based some of his characterization on a particularly stern tutor he had encountered during his theatrical training. Hopkins and Foster later reprised their roles in 2001's* Hannibal, *a sequel directed by Ridley Scott.*

2 Which film won Best Picture at the 69th Academy Awards, and Best Film at the 50th BAFTA awards, plus also earned Best Actor and Best Actress nominations for Ralph Fiennes and Kristin Scott Thomas in the same ceremonies?

The English Patient

3 Which actor, well known for appearing in Western films, produced, directed and starred in *Unforgiven*, later winning an Oscar and a Golden Globe for his direction?

Clint Eastwood

4 For which 1995 film did Mel Gibson win both an Oscar and a Golden Globe for his direction, and in which he starred as Sir William Wallace?

Braveheart

5 Which director won an Academy Award, Golden Globe and Director's Guild of America award for his direction of the film *American Beauty*?

Sam Mendes

6 Who wrote and directed *All About My Mother*, the 1999 Spanish-language winner of the Oscar for Best Foreign Language Film?

Pedro Almodóvar

7 Which 1994 film won six of the thirteen Academy Awards it had been nominated for, including Best Picture?

Forrest Gump

Oscar-winning Actors

QUESTIONS

1 Which actor won the Best Actor Oscar two years in a row, in 1993 and 1994?

2 In which 1992 adaptation of an E. M. Forster novel did Emma Thompson play the role of Margaret Schlegel, for which she won the Oscar for Best Actress?

3 In which 1990 adaptation of a Stephen King novel did Kathy Bates play obsessive nurse Annie Wilkes, earning the Oscar for Best Actress?

4 For her role in which film did Hilary Swank win the Oscar for Best Actress, in a movie based on the real-life story of Brandon Teena?

5 Who won Best Actor for his role in the 1992 drama *Scent of a Woman*, in which he played a blind, retired colonel?

6 Who won the Best Actress Oscar for her role in the 1995 crime drama *Dead Man Walking*, directed by Tim Robbins?

7 For which role did Anthony Hopkins win a Best Actor Oscar in 1991?

Oscar-winning Actors
ANSWERS

1 Which actor won the Best Actor Oscar two years in a row, in 1993 and 1994?

Tom Hanks

His first win was for the 1993 film Philadelphia, *which he followed with a win for his role as the titular* Forrest Gump *in 1994, which also won the Oscar for Best Picture. He was the second actor to accomplish the feat, after Spencer Tracy who had previously won in both 1938 and 1939.*

2 In which 1992 adaptation of an E. M. Forster novel did Emma Thompson play the role of Margaret Schlegel, for which she won the Oscar for Best Actress?

Howard's End

3 In which 1990 adaptation of a Stephen King novel did Kathy Bates play obsessive nurse Annie Wilkes, earning the Oscar for Best Actress?

Misery

4 For her role in which film did Hilary Swank win the Oscar for Best Actress, in a movie based on the real-life story of Brandon Teena?

Boys Don't Cry

5 Who won Best Actor for his role in the 1992 drama *Scent of a Woman*, in which he played a blind, retired colonel?

Al Pacino

6 Who won the Best Actress Oscar for her role in the 1995 crime drama *Dead Man Walking*, directed by Tim Robbins?

Susan Sarandon

7 For which role did Anthony Hopkins win a Best Actor Oscar in 1991?

Hannibal Lecter

Romcoms 2
QUESTIONS

1 In which 1998 film does Lindsay Lohan star as both of a set of identical twins attempting to rekindle romance between their long-separated parents?

2 Which actor won a Best Supporting Actor Oscar for his role in the 1996 film *Jerry Maguire*, well-remembered for a scene in which he encourages Tom Cruise's character to yell "Show me the money"?

3 Change one letter in each word below to reveal the name of a 1997 comedy-drama, for which lead actors Jack Nicholson and Helen Hunt won Oscars for Best Actor and Best Actress, respectively:

IS GOLD AT IF GUTS

4 Which song, written by Burt Bacharach for Dionne Warwick and later recorded by Aretha Franklin, features in *My Best Friend's Wedding*, and is sung by the cast in a restaurant scene?

5 Which two actors, who both had major roles in the TV show *Friends*, appeared together as the protagonists in the 1998 comedy drama *The Object of My Affection*?

6 "Catch her if you can" was the tagline used for which 1999 film starring Richard Gere and Julia Roberts?

7 On which Caribbean island does the titular character meet her love interest in *How Stella Got Her Groove Back*?

Romcoms 2
ANSWERS

1 In which 1998 film does Lindsay Lohan star as both of a set of identical twins attempting to rekindle romance between their long-separated parents?

The Parent Trap

With Natasha Richardson and Dennis Quaid as the girls' parents, the movie is a remake of the 1961 film of the same name which also starred a single actor—Hayley Mills—in the role of the twin daughters. Joanna Barnes appeared in both films: in the 1998 version she played the mother of her character in the original.

2 Which actor won a Best Supporting Actor Oscar for his role in the 1996 film *Jerry Maguire*, well-remembered for a scene in which he encourages Tom Cruise's character to yell "Show me the money"?

Cuba Gooding Jr.

3 Change one letter in each word below to reveal the name of a 1997 comedy-drama, for which lead actors Jack Nicholson and Helen Hunt won Oscars for Best Actor and Best Actress, respectively:

IS GOLD AT IF GUTS

As Good as It Gets

4 Which song, written by Burt Bacharach for Dionne Warwick and later recorded by Aretha Franklin, features in *My Best Friend's Wedding*, and is sung by the cast in a restaurant scene?

I Say a Little Prayer

5 Which two actors, who both had major roles in the TV show *Friends*, appeared together as the protagonists in the 1998 comedy drama *The Object of My Affection*?

Jennifer Aniston and Paul Rudd

6 "Catch her if you can" was the tagline used for which 1999 film starring Richard Gere and Julia Roberts?

Runaway Bride

7 On which Caribbean island does the titular character meet her love interest in *How Stella Got Her Groove Back*?

Jamaica

Brush with the Law
QUESTIONS

1 On which Caribbean island is the 1992 legal drama *A Few Good Men* set?

2 Change one letter in each word below to reveal the title of a 1996 legal drama based on a novel by John Grisham, which starred Sandra Bullock and Samuel L. Jackson:

I TILE SO TILL

3 Which 1993 comedy, starring Joe Pesci as the title character, depicts a newly qualified lawyer called in to defend family members who find themselves falsely accused of murder?

4 In which 1999 film, based on a Stephen King story, does Michael Clarke Duncan play a man blessed with miraculous healing abilities, who is wrongly sentenced to execution?

5 Which actor starred opposite Morgan Freeman in the 1995 psychological thriller *Seven*, as a detective tasked with investigating murders seemingly inspired by deadly sins?

6 What is the nickname of Morgan Freeman's character in 1994's *The Shawshank Redemption*?

7 Which 1995 thriller was advertised in promotional material prior to its release with the question "Who is Keyser Söze"?

Brush with the Law
ANSWERS

1 On which Caribbean island is the 1992 legal drama *A Few Good Men* set?

Cuba

> *Although set in a US naval base in Guantanamo Bay, the Cuban scenes were shot in southern California. Some 200 real marines were given permission to appear as extras in the movie, despite the production being denied permission to film at a real US military base.*

2 Change one letter in each word below to reveal the title of a 1996 legal drama based on a novel by John Grisham, which starred Sandra Bullock and Samuel L. Jackson:

I TILE SO TILL

A Time to Kill

3 Which 1993 comedy, starring Joe Pesci as the title character, depicts a newly qualified lawyer called in to defend family members who find themselves falsely accused of murder?

My Cousin Vinny

4 In which 1999 film, based on a Stephen King story, does Michael Clarke Duncan play a man blessed with miraculous healing abilities, who is wrongly sentenced to execution?

The Green Mile

5 Which actor starred opposite Morgan Freeman in the 1995 psychological thriller *Seven*, as a detective tasked with investigating murders seemingly inspired by deadly sins?

Brad Pitt

6 What is the nickname of Morgan Freeman's character in 1994's *The Shawshank Redemption*?

Red

7 Which 1995 thriller was advertised in promotional material prior to its release with the question "Who is Keyser Söze"?

The Usual Suspects

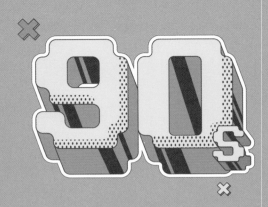

TV SHOWS

Get your Brain ready (and bring Pinky along for the ride!) as you work through the Absolutely Fabulous heyday of the sit-com, the sassy legal drama and the risqué cartoon comedy. The 90s was an era where canned laughter abounded, the "Rachel" was the only hairstyle worth having, and the eyes of the ranger were forever upon you.

Do you think you 9021-know everything there is to know about 90s TV? Well, bust out the cheesy poofs, put the Rugrats down for the night, and gather your Friends around to find out exactly Who's the Boss and who'll be up Dawson's Creek without a paddle. Just remember, the truth is out there!

Action & Drama
QUESTIONS

1. Which political drama, starring Martin Sheen as fictional US President Josiah "Jed" Bartlet, premiered in 1999?

2. Fill in the gaps below, one letter per gap, to restore the name of an Alaska-based comedy-drama which ran for six seasons:

   _O_T_E_N   _X_O_U_E

3. Which Emmy-winning drama, starring Dylan McDermott and LisaGay Hamilton, inspired the spin-off series *Boston Legal*?

4. Which cult mystery-horror drama, named after a fictional Washington town, initially ran for just two seasons, the first of which detailed an investigation into the murder of homecoming queen Laura Palmer?

5. Which one of these awards did Edie Falco *not* personally win for her role as Carmela Soprano in *The Sopranos*?

   a. SAG Award
   b. Primetime Emmy
   c. People's Choice Award
   d. Golden Globe

6. What is the name of the therapist first visited by Tony Soprano in the pilot episode of *The Sopranos*, with whom he explores the difficulties of life as a mobster?

7. Which actor, who later went on to appear as Mr. Big in the sitcom *Sex and the City*, played New York Detective Mike Logan in the first five seasons of *Law & Order*?

1 Which political drama, starring Martin Sheen as fictional US President Josiah "Jed" Bartlet, premiered in 1999?

The West Wing

While the character became integral to the show, which focused on daily life at The White House, creator Aaron Sorkin had not originally intended for the fictional president to play a major role in the series—or even to feature at all. Sheen later stated that he based much of his character on Bill Clinton, who was the serving US president when the show began.

2 Fill in the gaps below, one letter per gap, to restore the name of an Alaska-based comedy-drama which ran for six seasons:

_O_T_E_N   _X_O_U_E

Northern Exposure

3 Which Emmy-winning drama, starring Dylan McDermott and LisaGay Hamilton, inspired the spin-off series *Boston Legal*?

The Practice

4 Which cult mystery-horror drama, named after a fictional Washington town, initially ran for just two seasons, the first of which detailed an investigation into the murder of homecoming queen Laura Palmer?

Twin Peaks

5 Which one of these awards did Edie Falco *not* personally win for her role as Carmela Soprano in *The Sopranos*?

a. SAG Award
b. Primetime Emmy
c. People's Choice Award
d. Golden Globe

c. People's Choice Award

6 What is the name of the therapist first visited by Tony Soprano in the pilot episode of *The Sopranos*, with whom he explores the difficulties of life as a mobster?

Jennifer Melfi

7 Which actor, who later went on to appear as Mr. Big in the sitcom *Sex and the City*, played New York Detective Mike Logan in the first five seasons of *Law & Order*?

Chris Noth

Seinfeld 1
QUESTIONS

1 In which US city is *Seinfeld* set?

2 What is the first name of the character who is usually referred to by just his surname, Kramer?

3 How many times did *Seinfeld* win the Primetime Emmy for Outstanding Comedy Series?

4 In the episode *The Parking Garage*, what item has Kramer just purchased from the New Jersey shopping mall whose garage they cannot seem to leave?

5 Can you restore the missing letters in the following alias, occasionally used by George throughout the series, which has had several of its letters removed:

_R_ _A_D_L_Y

6 What is the job of recurring character, Newman, who lives directly down the hall from Seinfeld?

7 Which actor, who later went on to star in the comedy series *Veep*, plays the role of Seinfeld's former girlfriend Elaine Benes?

Seinfeld 1
ANSWERS

1 In which US city is *Seinfeld* set?

New York City, New York

Specifically, the show was set in the Upper West Side of Manhattan, although filming principally took place in California, at CBS's studio. Frequently described as "a show about nothing," Seinfeld's creators later said that they had come up with the show as a means of demonstrating how a comedian might gather material.

2 What is the first name of the character who is usually referred to by just his surname, Kramer?

Cosmo

3 How many times did *Seinfeld* win the Primetime Emmy for Outstanding Comedy Series?

Once, in 1993

4 In the episode *The Parking Garage*, what item has Kramer just purchased from the New Jersey shopping mall whose garage they cannot seem to leave?

An air conditioner

5 Can you restore the missing letters in the following alias, occasionally used by George throughout the series, which has had several of its letters removed:

_R_ _A_D_L_Y

Art Vandelay

6 What is the job of recurring character, Newman, who lives directly down the hall from Seinfeld?

Mailman

7 Which actor, who later went on to star in the comedy series *Veep*, plays the role of Seinfeld's former girlfriend Elaine Benes?

Julia Louis-Dreyfus

Out of This World
QUESTIONS

1 What is the name of the FBI special agent played by Gillian Anderson in the paranormal investigative drama, *The X-Files*?

2 "Signs and Portents" is the name of the first season of which sci-fi series, whose title takes most of its name from an ancient Mesopotamian city?

3 Which *Grey's Anatomy* actor played the part-alien character Isabel Evans in sci-fi drama *Roswell*?

4 Which of these titles is the correct styling for the name of the sci-fi series in which characters traveled almost instantly between distant locations in the cosmos, via an alien bridge device?

a. Stargate SGOne
b. Stargate S.G. 1
c. Stargate SG-1
d. StarGate SG - 1

5 Rearrange the letters below to reveal the title of a series in the *Star Trek* franchise which premiered in 1993, and which was set on board a space station of the same name:

ACE SPIN DEEPEN (4, 5, 4)

6 In the *Quantum Leap* episode *The Boogieman*, which real horror writer do the cast meet a younger fictionalized version of, who has a dog named Cujo?

7 Which Welsh actor, known for his roles in the *Lord of the Rings* and *Indiana Jones* film series, played Professor Maximillian Arturo in the wormhole-based *Sliders*?

Out of This World

1 What is the name of the FBI special agent played by Gillian Anderson in the paranormal investigative drama, *The X-Files*?

Dana Scully, MD

> *Known as Scully, the medical-doctor-turned-FBI-special-agent played by Anderson became so iconic that the character is purported to have led to the "Scully Effect," marked by an uptick in the numbers of women entering some STEM and law enforcement fields.*

2 "Signs and Portents" is the name of the first season of which sci-fi series, whose title takes most of its name from an ancient Mesopotamian city?

Babylon 5

3 Which *Grey's Anatomy* actor played the part-alien character Isabel Evans in sci-fi drama *Roswell*?

Katherine Heigl

4 Which of these titles is the correct styling for the name of the sci-fi series in which characters traveled almost instantly between distant locations in the cosmos, via an alien bridge device?

a. Stargate SGOne
b. Stargate S.G. 1
c. Stargate SG-1
d. StarGate SG - 1

c. *Stargate SG-1*

5 Rearrange the letters below to reveal the title of a series in the *Star Trek* franchise which premiered in 1993, and which was set on board a space station of the same name:

ACE SPIN DEEPEN (4, 5, 4)

Deep Space Nine

6 In the *Quantum Leap* episode *The Boogieman*, which real horror writer do the cast meet a younger fictionalized version of, who has a dog named Cujo?

Stephen King

7 Which Welsh actor, known for his roles in the *Lord of the Rings* and *Indiana Jones* film series, played Professor Maximillian Arturo in the wormhole-based *Sliders*?

John Rhys-Davies

Teen Soaps & Sitcoms

QUESTIONS

1. Which sitcom starring Will Smith begins with a rap he composed for the show, which features the opening line "Now this is a story all about how / My life got flip-turned upside-down"?

2. Which teen drama set in a Californian city contains a ZIP code as part of its title?

3. In *Sister, Sister*, what are the first names of the titular twins who were separated at birth but later reunited?

4. Which character from a US teen sitcom, named after its two leading actors, professed his love for orange soda by asking himself "Who loves orange soda?"?

5. Which actor, who later starred in the sitcom *How I Met Your Mother*, played his first major role as Nick in the short-lived comedy drama *Freaks and Geeks*?

6. Which sitcom, set at the fictional Bayside High School in Los Angeles, is a reworking of the earlier Disney Channel series *Good Morning, Miss Bliss*?

7. Which actor played the role of Joey Potter in *Dawson's Creek*, who becomes a love interest for the show's central protagonist?

Teen Soaps & Sitcoms
ANSWERS

1 Which sitcom starring Will Smith begins with a rap he composed for the show, which features the opening line "Now this is a story all about how / My life got flip-turned upside-down"?

The Fresh Prince of Bel Air

Smith wrote the lyrics, and performed the rap which plays over the opening credits with DJ Jazzy Jeff, giving a narrative of how his character came to live in Bel Air. The premise of the show is loosely based on the real-life experiences of its creator Benny Medina, and the theme tune was released as a single in the Netherlands and Spain.

2 Which teen drama set in a Californian city contains a ZIP code as part of its title?

Beverly Hills, 90210

3 In *Sister, Sister*, what are the first names of the titular twins who were separated at birth but later reunited?

Tia and Tamera

4 Which character from a US teen sitcom, named after its two leading actors, professed his love for orange soda by asking himself "Who loves orange soda?"?

Kel— from *Kenan and Kel*

5 Which actor, who later starred in the sitcom *How I Met Your Mother*, played his first major role as Nick in the short-lived comedy drama *Freaks and Geeks*?

Jason Segel

6 Which sitcom, set at the fictional Bayside High School in Los Angeles, is a reworking of the earlier Disney Channel series *Good Morning, Miss Bliss*?

Saved by the Bell

7 Which actor played the role of Joey Potter in *Dawson's Creek*, who becomes a love interest for the show's central protagonist?

Katie Holmes

SNL Stars
QUESTIONS

1 Which film, starring Mike Myers and Dana Carvey, began as a recurring SNL sketch featuring two rock music fans?

2 Premiering in 2005, *Everybody Hates Chris* was a sitcom based on the early life of which SNL star, who had appeared on the show from 1990 to 1993?

3 Which actor and comedian, who first appeared on SNL in 1990, was fired five years later—before going on to star in the film *Happy Gilmore* the following year?

4 Which actress and *Singin' in the Rain* star did Cheri Oteri impersonate in the 1995 sketch "Leg Up"?

5 Which comedian starred as the character Jacobim Mugatu in the film *Zoolander*, alongside fellow SNL alumnus Ben Stiller?

6 During her time on SNL, which cast member starred in an episode of Seinfeld as a co-worker of the character Elaine, notable for the fact that she did not swing her arms when she walked?

7 Rearrange the letters below to restore the name of a recurring SNL sketch in which David Spade starred as a reporter mocking celebrities:

LOONY TEDIUM HOWL (9, 6)

SNL Stars
ANSWERS

1 Which film, starring Mike Myers and Dana Carvey, began as a recurring SNL sketch featuring two rock music fans?

Wayne's World

Based on a recurring SNL sketch of the same name, the film featured the characters of Wayne and Garth, rock fans who broadcast their own TV show. One of the best-known original sketches saw the pair joined by the band Aerosmith, and also guest-starred Tom Hanks as one of the band's roadies.

2 Premiering in 2005, *Everybody Hates Chris* was a sitcom based on the early life of which SNL star, who had appeared on the show from 1990 to 1993?

Chris Rock

3 Which actor and comedian, who first appeared on SNL in 1990, was fired five years later—before going on to star in the film *Happy Gilmore* the following year?

Adam Sandler

4 Which actress and *Singin' in the Rain* star did Cheri Oteri impersonate in the 1995 sketch "Leg Up"?

Debbie Reynolds

5 Which comedian starred as the character Jacobim Mugatu in the film *Zoolander*, alongside fellow SNL alumnus Ben Stiller?

Will Ferrell

6 During her time on SNL, which cast member starred in an episode of Seinfeld as a co-worker of the character Elaine, notable for the fact that she did not swing her arms when she walked?

Molly Shannon

7 Rearrange the letters below to restore the name of a recurring SNL sketch in which David Spade starred as a reporter mocking celebrities:

LOONY TEDIUM HOWL (9, 6)

Hollywood Minute

Friends 1
QUESTIONS

1 In what year was the pilot of *Friends* first broadcast?

2 Which English actor played the role of Ross's second wife, Emily?

3 What are the names of Ross and Monica's parents?

4 In which luxury New York City department store does Rachel begin working after quitting her job as a waitress?

5 In which cafe did the six friends regularly meet, whose name was a pun on a New York City landmark?

6 What is the name of the cafe's main barista, played by actor James Michael Tyler?

7 Which of these titles was *not* considered as an early title for the show?

a. Insomnia Cafe
b. People We Know
c. Six Of One
d. Friends Like Us

8 Which of Phoebe's songs is first performed in season two's *The One Where Eddie Moves In*?

9 In which season of *Friends* did Joey first use his catchphrase pick-up line, "How *you* doin'"?

Friends 1
ANSWERS

1 In what year was the pilot of *Friends* first broadcast?

1994

> *The first episode premiered on NBC on September 22nd. It was written by Marta Kauffman and David Crane, and directed by James Burrows who was perhaps best known at the time for directing the Boston-based hit comedy Cheers. Filmed in California and yet set in New York City's Manhattan district, the pilot episode was watched by 22 million viewers.*

2 Which English actor played the role of Ross's second wife, Emily?

Helen Baxendale

3 What are the names of Ross and Monica's parents?

Jack and Judy Geller

4 In which luxury New York City department store does Rachel begin working after quitting her job as a waitress?

Bloomingdale's

5 In which cafe did the six friends regularly meet, whose name was a pun on a New York City landmark?

Central Perk

6 What is the name of the cafe's main barista, played by actor James Michael Tyler?

Gunther

7 Which of these titles was *not* considered as an early title for the show?

a. Insomnia Cafe
b. People We Know
c. Six Of One
d. Friends Like Us

b. People We Know

8 Which of Phoebe's songs is first performed in season two's *The One Where Eddie Moves In*?

Smelly Cat

9 In which season of Friends did Joey first use his catchphrase pick-up line, "How *you* doin'"?

Season 4—in episode 13, *The One with Rachel's Crush*

Medical Dramas
QUESTIONS

1. What was the name of the character played by George Clooney in *E.R.*, who works as a pediatrician in the show's emergency department?

2. Which British medical drama, set in a hospital in the fictional English county of Wyvern, launched in 1999 as a spin-off from the long-running *Casualty*, also set in the same hospital?

3. Fill in the gaps below, with one letter per gap, to reveal the name of a US soap opera with a medically related name that celebrated its 35th year of broadcast in 1998, commemorated with a one-off primetime special?

   _E_E_A_ _ _O_P_T_L

4. Which novel, written by *E.R.* creator Michael Crichton, went on to become a blockbuster movie of the same title, starring Sam Neill and directed by Steven Spielberg?

5. For which medical soap opera, which has a US city in its name, did Mandy Patinkin win a Primetime Emmy for Outstanding Lead Actor in a Drama Series in 1995?

6. Which actor played the titular role in *Dougie Howser, M.D.*, and was 16 years old at the start of filming?

7. Which medical crime drama series, starring Dick Van Dyke and his real-life son as a crime-solving duo, debuted in 1993?

Medical Dramas
ANSWERS

1 What was the name of the character played by George Clooney in *E.R.*, who works as a pediatrician in the show's emergency department?

Dr. Doug Ross

In the pilot episode in 1994, this breakout role saw George Clooney's character arrive in the ER to be treated for drunkenness, an apparent symptom of St. Patrick's Day. Although his character officially departed for Seattle after five seasons, Clooney returned twice to the show in later seasons, on the proviso that his name and face were not used in advance to promote the surprise reappearances.

2 Which British medical drama, set in a hospital in the fictional English county of Wyvern, launched in 1999 as a spin-off from the long-running *Casualty*, also set in the same hospital?

Holby City

3 Fill in the gaps below, with one letter per gap, to reveal the name of a US soap opera with a medically related name that celebrated its 35th year of broadcast in 1998, commemorated with a one-off primetime special?

_E_A_ _O_P_T_L

General Hospital

4 Which novel, written by *E.R.* creator Michael Crichton, went on to become a blockbuster movie of the same title, starring Sam Neill and directed by Steven Spielberg?

Jurassic Park

5 For which medical soap opera, which has a US city in its name, did Mandy Patinkin win a Primetime Emmy for Outstanding Lead Actor in a Drama Series in 1995?

Chicago Hope

6 Which actor played the titular role in *Dougie Howser, M.D.*, and was 16 years old at the start of filming?

Neil Patrick Harris

7 Which medical crime drama series, starring Dick Van Dyke and his real-life son as a crime-solving duo, debuted in 1993?

Diagnosis: Murder

Iconic Taglines

QUESTIONS

Can you name each of the TV shows which featured the following iconic taglines during their original runs?

1 "Domestic bliss was never like this!"

2 "New faces and dangerous places!"

3 "Divided by Destiny. Bound by Love."

4 "The legend begins"

5 "The truth is out there"

6 "In the complex process of determining guilt and innocence, lives often hang in the balance"

7 "Everyone's life could use a touch of magic"

Iconic Taglines
ANSWERS

Can you name each of the TV shows which featured the following iconic taglines during their original runs?

1 "Domestic bliss was never like this!"

Married... with Children

> *Although the show first launched in 1987, it ran until 1997 which therefore makes it one of the longest-running US primetime sitcoms of all time. There was also an additional episode first broadcast in the US in 2002, having been held back from its originally intended 1989 air date due to a censorship dispute over its content.*

2 "New faces and dangerous places!"

Beverly Hills, 90210

3 "Divided by Destiny. Bound by Love."

Buffy the Vampire Slayer

4 "The legend begins"

Batman: The Animated Series

5 "The truth is out there"

The X-Files

6 "In the complex process of determining guilt and innocence, lives often hang in the balance"

Law & Order

7 "Everyone's life could use a touch of magic"

Sabrina the Teenage Witch

Sitcoms 1
QUESTIONS

1. Which British comedian plays the role of Edina Monsoon in *Absolutely Fabulous*, a character based on a sketch created with comedy partner Dawn French?

2. Which sitcom won five consecutive Primetime Emmy Awards for Outstanding Comedy Series in the 1990s?

3. In the eponymous sitcom *Ellen*, what is the profession of the show's protagonist, played by Ellen DeGeneres?

4. In which US state is *That 70's Show* set, which premiered in 1998?

5. In *Everybody Loves Raymond*, what is the name of Raymond's wife, played by Patricia Heaton?

6. Who are the titular characters, played by Eric McCormack and Debra Messing, in a New-York based sitcom which debuted in 1998, focusing on the friendship between a gay lawyer and a straight interior designer?

7. Which Chicago-based sitcom, that ran from 1989 to 1998 and starred an ensemble cast, is a spin-off from *Perfect Strangers*?

Sitcoms 1
ANSWERS

1 Which British comedian plays the role of Edina Monsoon in *Absolutely Fabulous*, a character based on a sketch created with comedy partner Dawn French?

Jennifer Saunders

Based on the sketch Modern Mother and Daughter *from the hit comedy show* French and Saunders, Absolutely Fabulous *follows the antics of thrill-seeking Edina Monsoon, friend to Patsy Stone and mother to Saffy. According to Saunders, the character was inspired by the band Bananarama, with whom the comedy duo had worked on a charity comedy special in the late 1980s.*

2 Which sitcom won five consecutive Primetime Emmy Awards for Outstanding Comedy Series in the 1990s?

Frasier

3 In the eponymous sitcom *Ellen*, what is the profession of the show's protagonist, played by Ellen DeGeneres?

Bookstore owner

4 In which US state is *That 70's Show* set, which premiered in 1998?

Wisconsin

5 In *Everybody Loves Raymond*, what is the name of Raymond's wife, played by Patricia Heaton?

Debra Barone

6 Who are the titular characters, played by Eric McCormack and Debra Messing, in a New-York based sitcom which debuted in 1998, focusing on the friendship between a gay lawyer and a straight interior designer?

Will Truman and Grace Adler, from *Will & Grace*

7 Which Chicago-based sitcom, that ran from 1989 to 1998 and starred an ensemble cast, is a spin-off from *Perfect Strangers*?

Family Matters

Supernatural
QUESTIONS

1. What is the name of Sabrina's black cat in *Sabrina the Teenage Witch*, who shares their name with a Massachusetts town that is often connected to witchcraft?

2. In the title of the 1999 supernatural crime drama *G vs. E*, what do the two initials stand for?

3. In which fictional California town is *Buffy the Vampire Slayer* set?

4. Which of these groups of three names gives the correct first names of the Halliwell sisters, who appear in the fantasy drama series *Charmed*?

   a. Pepper, Prim, and Persephone
   b. Pippa, Pat, and Pallas
   c. Piper, Prue, and Phoebe
   d. Porter, Paige, and Penelope

5. Fill in the gaps below, with one letter per gap, to reveal the name of a macabre soap opera set in a gothic Maine mansion, which first aired in 1991:

   _A_K   _H_D_W_

6. Which *Buffy the Vampire Slayer* character became the focus of a spin-off show, which subsequently ran for five seasons after a 1998 premiere?

7. Which Shakespeare play provided the inspiration for the title of *Charmed*'s first episode, "Something Wicca This Way Comes"?

1 What is the name of Sabrina's black cat in *Sabrina the Teenage Witch*, who shares their name with a Massachusetts town that is often connected to witchcraft?

Salem

> *Gifted with the power of speech, the black cat owned by Sabrina and her aunts is portrayed as dryly witty. The cat is, in fact, a sorcerer sentenced to live for a century in a feline form without magical powers. The town of Salem in Massachusetts is infamous for its 17th-century witch trials.*

2 In the title of the 1999 supernatural crime drama *G vs. E*, what do the two initials stand for?

Good and Evil

3 In which fictional California town is *Buffy the Vampire Slayer* set?

Sunnydale

4 Which of these groups of three names gives the correct first names of the Halliwell sisters, who appear in the fantasy drama series *Charmed*?

a. Pepper, Prim, and Persephone
b. Pippa, Pat, and Pallas
c. Piper, Prue, and Phoebe
d. Porter, Paige, and Penelope

c. Piper, Prue and Phoebe

5 Fill in the gaps below, with one letter per gap, to reveal the name of a macabre soap opera set in a gothic Maine mansion, which first aired in 1991:

_A_K _H_D_W_

Dark Shadows

6 Which *Buffy the Vampire Slayer* character became the focus of a spin-off show, which subsequently ran for five seasons after a 1998 premiere?

Angel

7 Which Shakespeare play provided the inspiration for the title of *Charmed*'s first episode, "Something Wicca This Way Comes"?

Macbeth

Theme Tunes
QUESTIONS

1 Which two foods are mentioned in the words to *Frasier*'s closing theme song?

2 Which TV show's theme tune begins with the lyric, "Whatever happened to predictability"?

3 How many words are sung during the entire opening theme of *The Simpsons*?

4 In *The Fresh Prince of Bel-Air*'s theme song, where does Will Smith's character describe himself as having been "born and raised"?

5 *Searching My Soul* is the name of the track played as which show's theme tune, whose title is the name of its main protagonist?

6 Which Academy-Award-winning actor and musician can be heard singing the opening theme to *Married... With Children*?

7 How many quick, successive claps can be heard after the first line of the *Friends* theme tune is sung?

Theme Tunes

ANSWERS

1 Which two foods are mentioned in the words to *Frasier*'s closing theme song?

Tossed salads and scrambled eggs

Sung by the show's lead actor Kelsey Grammer, the mixed-up nature of the foods is intended as a reference to the mental states of the callers who contact psychiatrist Frasier's character. The song was performed in Spanish at the end of one of the show's fifth season-episodes, becoming the only time it was not performed by Grammer himself.

2 Which TV show's theme tune begins with the lyric, "Whatever happened to predictability"?

Full House

3 How many words are sung during the entire opening theme of *The Simpsons*?

Two: "The" and "Simpsons"

4 In *The Fresh Prince of Bel-Air*'s theme song, where does Will Smith's character describe himself as having been "born and raised"?

West Philadelphia

5 *Searching My Soul* is the name of the track played as which show's theme tune, whose title is the name of its main protagonist?

Ally McBeal

6 Which Academy-Award-winning actor and musician can be heard singing the opening theme to *Married... With Children*?

Frank Sinatra

7 How many quick, successive claps can be heard after the first line of the *Friends* theme tune is sung?

Four

US Talk Shows
QUESTIONS

1. Which actress, known for her portrayal of Tracy Turnblad in the 1988 film *Hairspray*, debuted in 1993 as the host of a talk show bearing her own name, aged just 24?

2. Which Academy-Award winning actress hosted her own talk show from 1992 to 1993, featuring Elizabeth Taylor as a guest in the very first episode?

3. Which talk show, hosted by a Canadian actress and running from 1991 to 2003, featured the first TV appearances of musicians Usher, Ludacris, and Nelly?

4. Change one letter in each word to reveal the rhyming title of a spoof animated talk show, which premiered in 1994 and featured fictional superheroes talking about their powers:

   SPICE GLOST BOAST SO ROAST

5. Having won six Primetime Emmys for Outstanding Variety, Music or Comedy Series, which talk show was replaced by the similarly titled *The Late Show with Stephen Colbert*, following the retirement of its host?

6. What is the name of the talk show host whose eponymous series, running from 1991 to 2018, spawned a 2003 British musical opera spoof which also bore his name?

7. From which talk show, debuting in 1991 and retitled to just a one-word name in 1998, did the oft-repeated assertion "You are *not* the father" become a well-known phrase?

1 Which actress, known for her portrayal of Tracy Turnblad in the 1988 film *Hairspray*, debuted in 1993 as the host of a talk show bearing her own name, aged just 24?

Ricki Lake

At the time, Lake was believed to be the youngest person to have hosted their own talk show. Ricki Lake originally aired from 1993 to 2004 and famously featured a "doorbell" segment with a door leading onto the stage, through which the show's guests might suddenly find themselves confronted with a second guest wanting to set the story straight.

2 Which Academy-Award winning actress hosted her own talk show from 1992 to 1993, featuring Elizabeth Taylor as a guest in the very first episode?

Whoopi Goldberg

3 Which talk show, hosted by a Canadian actress and running from 1991 to 2003, featured the first TV appearances of musicians Usher, Ludacris, and Nelly?

The Jenny Jones Show

4 Change one letter in each word to reveal the rhyming title of a spoof animated talk show, which premiered in 1994 and featured fictional superheroes talking about their powers:

SPICE GLOST BOAST SO ROAST

Space Ghost Coast to Coast

5 Having won six Primetime Emmys for Outstanding Variety, Music or Comedy Series, which talk show was replaced by the similarly titled *The Late Show with Stephen Colbert*, following the retirement of its host?

The Late Show with David Letterman

6 What is the name of the talk show host whose eponymous series, running from 1991 to 2018, spawned a 2003 British musical opera spoof which also bore his name?

Jerry Springer

7 From which talk show, debuting in 1991 and retitled to just a one-word name in 1998, did the oft-repeated assertion "You are *not* the father" become a well-known phrase?

Maury, first known as The Maury Povich Show

Kids' Cartoons 1
QUESTIONS

1 What are the names of the three Powerpuff Girls?

2 In *Dexter's Laboratory*, what is the name of the main character's ballet-dancing older sister, who frequently breaks into his workspace and ruins his experiments?

3 What unusual talent is the protagonist Eliza gifted with in *The Wild Thornberrys*, allowing her to make a wide variety of friends during her family's travels?

4 In a popular cartoon, who lives in a pineapple under the sea?

5 In the anthropomorphic cartoon *Arthur*, what kind of animals are the titular character and his sister D.W.?

6 Rearrange the letters below to reveal the name of the three-year-old antagonist in an animated series which ran for nine seasons, from 1991 to 2004:

PICKS ALLEGIANCE (8, 7)

7 Which animated cartoon features two genetically modified mice, one of which is determined to achieve world domination, and was executive-produced by Steven Spielberg for its entire run from 1995 to 1998?

Kids' Cartoons 1
ANSWERS

1 What are the names of the three Powerpuff Girls?

Bubbles, Blossom, and Buttercup

> *According to the show, the three girls were accidentally created by a professor who was attempting to create "the perfect little girl". By adding the mysterious "Chemical X" to a mix of sugar, spice, and everything nice, the three girls were gifted with various superpowers, ranging from flight to X-ray vision.*

2 In *Dexter's Laboratory*, what is the name of the main character's ballet-dancing older sister, who frequently breaks into his workspace and ruins his experiments?

Dee Dee

3 What unusual talent is the protagonist Eliza gifted with in *The Wild Thornberrys*, allowing her to make a wide variety of friends during her family's travels?

The ability to speak to animals

4 In a popular cartoon, who lives in a pineapple under the sea?

SpongeBob SquarePants

5 In the anthropomorphic cartoon *Arthur*, what kind of animals are the titular character and his sister D.W.?

Aardvarks

6 Rearrange the letters below to reveal the name of the three-year-old antagonist in an animated series which ran for nine seasons, from 1991 to 2004:

PICKS ALLEGIANCE (8, 7)

Angelica Pickles, from *The Rugrats*

7 Which animated cartoon features two genetically modified mice, one of which is determined to achieve world domination, and was executive-produced by Steven Spielberg for its entire run from 1995 to 1998?

Pinky and the Brain

Game Shows
QUESTIONS

1 Which British game show, hosted by singer Cilla Black and running throughout the 1990s, featured three contestants vying to win an often-overseas trip with a fourth contestant who was hidden from view until the last moment?

2 Who was the host of US game show *Family Feud* during its first revival, that ran until 1993?

3 Which game show, first hosted by Chris Tarrant in its original UK version, was later hosted in the US by Regis Philbin?

4 Rearrange the letters below to reveal the title of a UK game show, hosted by Bob Monkhouse from 1993 to 1997, based on a US show with a Los Angeles neighborhood in its title:

CARELESS QUERY BIT
(9, 7)

5 Which long-running, iconic British game show, broadcast throughout the 1990s, was inspired by a similar French program whose name translates to *Numbers and Letters*?

6 Which alliteratively titled US game show, hosted by David Ruprecht, spawned a British spin-off with the same name, from 1993 until 2001?

7 In which long-running US game show, which continued to be aired throughout the 1990s, must contestants provide their answers in the form of a question?

Game Shows

ANSWERS

1 Which British game show, hosted by singer Cilla Black and running throughout the 1990s, featured three contestants vying to win an often-overseas trip with a fourth contestant who was hidden from view until the last moment?

Blind Date

> With her oft-repeated line, "What's your name and where do you come from?", Cilla Black introduced hundreds of would-be daters on the Saturday-night show, that originally ran from 1985 to 2003. Lucky couples could be sent as far away as the Maldives on their first dates—although one unfortunate contestant took a trip to Nepal alone in 1997, after being stood up at the airport.

2 Who was the host of US game show *Family Feud* during its first revival, that ran until 1993?

Ray Combs

3 Which game show, first hosted by Chris Tarrant in its original UK version, was later hosted in the US by Regis Philbin?

Who Wants to Be a Millionaire

4 Rearrange the letters below to reveal the title of a UK game show, hosted by Bob Monkhouse from 1993 to 1997, based on a US show with a Los Angeles neighborhood in its title:

CARELESS QUERY BIT (9, 7)

Celebrity Squares*, based on *Hollywood Squares

5 Which long-running, iconic British game show, broadcast throughout the 1990s, was inspired by a similar French program whose name translates to *Numbers and Letters*?

Countdown

6 Which alliteratively titled US game show, hosted by David Ruprecht, spawned a British spin-off with the same name, from 1993 until 2001?

Supermarket Sweep

7 In which long-running US game show, which continued to be aired throughout the 1990s, must contestants provide their answers in the form of a question?

Jeopardy!

Unlucky in Love
QUESTIONS

1. Which character played by Lisa Kudrow appears in both *Mad About You* and *Friends*?

2. Aside from the four leading women, who is the only character to appear in both the pilot and final episodes of *Sex and the City*?

3. In the pilot episode of *Friends*, what is the name of the colleague Monica dates, who has a nickname related to his role at work?

4. What is the name of the Boston law firm which Ally McBeal joins in the 1997 pilot episode, in the series of the same name?

5. In *Mad About You*, what name do Paul and Jamie give to their daughter in the show's sixth season?

6. Which actor and rapper, known for her roles in the film musicals *Chicago* and *Hairspray*, starred as Khadijah James in the Boston-based sitcom *Living Single*?

7. Which *Dawson's Creek* character, played by Michelle Williams, arrives from New York City in the pilot episode, creating an apparent love triangle with Dawson and his friend Joey?

1 Which character played by Lisa Kudrow appears in both *Mad About You* and *Friends*?

Ursula Buffay

> *First appearing in* Mad About You *as a nonchalant waitress, the character later appeared in* Friends *as the twin sister of lead character Phoebe, both being played by Lisa Kudrow. In an apparent crossover, Helen Hunt appears as a guest star in a 1995 episode of* Friends *in which she mistakes Phoebe for Ursula.*

2 Aside from the four leading women, who is the only character to appear in both the pilot and final episodes of *Sex and the City*?

Mr. Big

3 In the pilot episode of *Friends*, what is the name of the colleague Monica dates, who has a nickname related to his role at work?

Paul the Wine Guy

4 What is the name of the Boston law firm which Ally McBeal joins in the 1997 pilot episode, in the series of the same name?

Cage & Fish

5 In *Mad About You*, what name do Paul and Jamie give to their daughter in the show's sixth season?

Mabel

6 Which actor and rapper, known for her roles in the film musicals *Chicago* and *Hairspray*, starred as Khadijah James in the Boston-based sitcom *Living Single*?

Queen Latifah

7 Which *Dawson's Creek* character, played by Michelle Williams, arrives from New York City in the pilot episode, creating an apparent love triangle with Dawson and his friend Joey?

Jen Lindley

Animated Sitcoms
QUESTIONS

1. In which fictional town do the residents of the long-running show *The Simpsons* live?

2. Which actor, best known for his voice roles in *The Lion King* and the *Star Wars* films, appeared as a guest star in *The Simpsons* for the first time in the early 1990s?

3. Change one letter in each word below to reveal the title of an animated sitcom which has featured guest stars Tom Petty and Alan Rickman:

    KIND IF SHE HELL

4. *Daria* is a spin-off of which alliteratively titled series that stars Mike Judge as both of the two dim-witted protagonists?

5. In *Family Guy*, what is the name of the Griffin family's talking dog, voiced by the show's creator Seth MacFarlane?

6. What was the name of the parka-wearing *South Park* character who was frequently killed off in the first seasons of the show, only to be inexplicably resurrected in each following episode?

7. Which animated sci-fi sitcom, created by Matt Groening, is set in New York City in the 31st century, and follows the adventures of the once-cryogenically-frozen character, Fry?

Animated Sitcoms
ANSWERS

1 In which fictional town do the residents of the long-running show *The Simpsons* live?

Springfield

> *The show's home town is never mentioned as being in a particular state, however, with the name Springfield partly being chosen due to how common it was across the US. Much of the city can be seen from above during the opening credits sequence, after the parting of white clouds reveals the iconic title card.*

2 Which actor, best known for his voice roles in *The Lion King* and the *Star Wars* films, appeared as a guest star in *The Simpsons* for the first time in the early 1990s?

James Earl Jones

3 Change one letter in each word below to reveal the title of an animated sitcom which has featured guest stars Tom Petty and Alan Rickman:

KIND IF SHE HELL

King of the Hill

4 *Daria* is a spin-off of which alliteratively titled series that stars Mike Judge as both of the two dim-witted protagonists?

Beavis and Butt-Head

5 In *Family Guy*, what is the name of the Griffin family's talking dog, voiced by the show's creator Seth MacFarlane?

Brian

6 What was the name of the parka-wearing *South Park* character who was frequently killed off in the first seasons of the show, only to be inexplicably resurrected in each following episode?

Kenny

7 Which animated sci-fi sitcom, created by Matt Groening, is set in New York City in the 31st century, and follows the adventures of the once-cryogenically-frozen character, Fry?

Futurama

Cameos
QUESTIONS

1 Which British comedian, who later went on to star in *House*, appeared in a 1998 episode of *Friends* alongside series regular Jennifer Aniston?

2 Which original *Star Wars* actress, who later worked unofficially on scripts for the films *Hook* and *Sister Act*, played a cameo voice role in *Frasier* as one of the titular psychiatrist's call-in patients?

3 Fill in the gaps below, with one letter per gap, to reveal the name of a comic actor who made appearances in *Friends*, *Seinfeld*, *The Simpsons* and *Married... with Children*, among many others:

_O_ _O_I_Z

4 In which popular romcom series did Jon Bon Jovi appear in a cameo role in 1999, playing another patient in the office of the leading character's therapist?

5 Which basketball player hosted an episode of *Saturday Night Live* in 1991, joking in his monologue about hypothetical sponsorship deals he turned down over the years?

6 What is the stage name of the well-known actor and wrestler who appeared in an episode of *That 70's Show*, playing his own famous wrestler father?

7 Which Boston-born actor, best known for a *Star Trek* role which he reprised for almost fifty years, appeared as himself in an episode of *The Simpsons*?

Cameos

ANSWERS

1 Which British comedian, who later went on to star in *House*, appeared in a 1998 episode of *Friends* alongside series regular Jennifer Aniston?

Hugh Laurie

> *In the season 4 finale episode,* The One with Ross's Wedding, *Part 2, Laurie sits on a plane next to Aniston's character, Rachel, as she flies to London to attend a wedding. Eavesdropping on her conversation with another passenger, he states "oh and by the way, it's clear you were on a break", in reference to a debate which carried on throughout much of the show's long run.*

2 Which original *Star Wars* actress, who later worked unofficially on scripts for the films *Hook* and *Sister Act*, played a cameo voice role in *Frasier* as one of the titular psychiatrist's call-in patients?

Carrie Fisher

3 Fill in the gaps below, with one letter per gap, to reveal the name of a comic actor who made appearances in *Friends*, *Seinfeld*, *The Simpsons* and *Married... with Children*, among many others:

_O_ _O_I_Z

Jon Lovitz

4 In which popular romcom series did Jon Bon Jovi appear in a cameo role in 1999, playing another patient in the office of the leading character's therapist?

Sex and the City

5 Which basketball player hosted an episode of Saturday Night Live in 1991, joking in his monologue about hypothetical sponsorship deals he turned down over the years?

Michael Jordan

6 What is the stage name of the well-known actor and wrestler who appeared in an episode of *That 70's Show*, playing his own famous wrestler father?

The Rock

7 Which Boston-born actor, best known for a *Star Trek* role which he reprised for almost fifty years, appeared as himself in an episode of *The Simpsons*?

Leonard Nimoy

Frasier

QUESTIONS

1. Which popular Boston-based comedy series is *Frasier* a spin-off from?

2. From which UK city does Daphne Moon, Frasier's sister-in-law played by Jane Leeves, emigrate to the USA?

3. Frasier's sofa is an exact replica of one owned by which famous French fashion designer with an alliterative name?

4. What was Frasier's father Martin Crane's profession, before he retired with mobility problems?

5. Which radio station hosts Frasier's daily psychotherapeutic broadcast, *The Dr. Frasier Crane Show*?

6. Which US actor, best known for a 1970s sitcom bearing her own name, performed a voice-only role on the show as one of Frasier's patients, named on air as Marjorie?

7. What is the name of the iconic Seattle observation tower which can be seen from Frasier's apartment, and which features on the show's title card?

1 Which popular Boston-based comedy series is *Frasier* a spin-off from?

Cheers

The character of Frasier Crane first appeared in Cheers as a love interest for Diane Chambers. Frasier is, however, set on the other side of the USA in Seattle, in a move from the production company to ensure that the new spin-off did not resemble Cheers too closely. In fact, however, several of the original Cheers cast members made cameo appearances on Frasier during the show's decade-long run.

2 From which UK city does Daphne Moon, Frasier's sister-in-law played by Jane Leeves, emigrate to the USA?

Manchester

3 Frasier's sofa is an exact replica of one owned by which famous French fashion designer with an alliterative name?

Coco Chanel

4 What was Frasier's father Martin Crane's profession, before he retired with mobility problems?

Police detective

5 Which radio station hosts Frasier's daily psychotherapeutic broadcast, *The Dr. Frasier Crane Show*?

KACL

6 Which US actor, best known for a 1970s sitcom bearing her own name, performed a voice-only role on the show as one of Frasier's patients, named on air as Marjorie?

Mary Tyler Moore

7 What is the name of the iconic Seattle observation tower which can be seen from Frasier's apartment, and which features on the show's title card?

The Space Needle

Comic-strip Shows
QUESTIONS

1. Which Marvel comic-book series, created by Stan Lee, was revived in a 1994 animated series that ran for two years and starred characters known as The Invisible Woman and The Human Torch?

2. Which superhero was voiced by Christopher Daniel Barnes, known for his role as Prince Eric in the 1989 film *The Little Mermaid*, during the five-season run of an eponymous animated series based on the original Marvel comics?

3. Delete one letter in each pair beneath to reveal the name of an animated series, based on a Marvel character, which ran from 1994 to 1996 and played as one half of *The Marvel Action Hour*:

   SI RP IO DN EM RA MN

4. Which actor, best known for his portrayal of Luke Skywalker in the *Star Wars* films, voiced The Joker in *Batman: The Animated Series*, which ran from 1992 to 1995?

5. By what name is Dr. Bruce Banner better known, which appeared in the title of an animated Marvel series from 1996 to 1997?

6. On what planet, named after a type of mathematical surface, is the 1993 to 1994 *Sonic the Hedgehog* TV series set?

7. With which animated show, running from 1992 to 1997, are the characters Rogue, Storm, and Wolverine most associated?

Comic-strip Shows

1 Which Marvel comic-book series, created by Stan Lee, was revived in a 1994 animated series that ran for two years and starred characters known as The Invisible Woman and The Human Torch?

Fantastic Four

> *The 1994 debut was the third made-for-TV-animation of the* Fantastic Four *comic book series, and featured the voice of creator Stan Lee as himself. Lori Alan, who voiced the Invisible Woman, also voiced characters for the hit 1990s animated series* SpongeBob SquarePants *and* Family Guy.

2 Which superhero was voiced by Christopher Daniel Barnes, known for his role as Prince Eric in the 1989 film *The Little Mermaid*, during the five-season run of an eponymous animated series based on the original Marvel comics?

Spider-Man

3 Delete one letter in each pair beneath to reveal the name of an animated series, based on a Marvel character, which ran from 1994 to 1996 and played as one half of *The Marvel Action Hour*:

SI RP IO DN EM RA MN

Iron Man

4 Which actor, best known for his portrayal of Luke Skywalker in the *Star Wars* films, voiced The Joker in *Batman: The Animated Series*, which ran from 1992 to 1995?

Mark Hamill

5 By what name is Dr. Bruce Banner better known, which appeared in the title of an animated Marvel series from 1996 to 1997?

The Hulk, or The Incredible Hulk

6 On what planet, named after a type of mathematical surface, is the 1993 to 1994 *Sonic the Hedgehog* TV series set?

Mobius

7 With which animated show, running from 1992 to 1997, are the characters Rogue, Storm, and Wolverine most associated?

X-Men

Seinfeld 2
QUESTIONS

1. Which actor and former *Saturday Night Live* writer co-created *Seinfeld* with fellow comedian Jerry Seinfeld?

2. In which US state do Seinfeld's parents, Morty and Helen, reside?

3. Which comic-book character is Seinfeld frequently shown to be a fan of?

4. What is the title of the episode, sharing much of its name with the play by Harold Pinter which inspired it, in which the action is presented in reverse chronological order?

5. Rearrange the letters below to reveal the name of an actor who played one of Seinfeld's love interests, and went on to star in the comedy *Will and Grace*:

   DRESSING BEAM (5, 7)

6. In the fifth season, what profession does George pretend to have in order to impress a college crush, which is then called into question during an incident on a beach?

7. Which of the show's episodes—out of a total of 180—are the only two in which the character Kramer does not appear?

Seinfeld 2
ANSWERS

1 Which actor and former *Saturday Night Live* writer co-created *Seinfeld* with fellow comedian Jerry Seinfeld?

Larry David

Although he did not appear in any credited roles in Seinfeld, *he did make some cameo appearances in the series, and was the voice of George's Yankees boss, George Steinbrenner. After* Seinfeld *had finished airing, Larry David later played the lead character in the show* Curb Your Enthusiasm, *which revisits many of the themes previously featured in* Seinfeld.

2 In which US state do Seinfeld's parents, Morty and Helen, reside?

Florida

3 Which comic-book character is Seinfeld frequently shown to be a fan of?

Superman

4 What is the title of the episode, sharing much of its name with the play by Harold Pinter which inspired it, in which the action is presented in reverse chronological order?

The Betrayal

5 Rearrange the letters below to reveal the name of an actor who played one of Seinfeld's love interests, and went on to star in the comedy *Will and Grace*:

DRESSING BEAM (5, 7)

Debra Messing

6 In the fifth season, what profession does George pretend to have in order to impress a college crush, which is then called into question during an incident on a beach?

Marine biologist

7 Which of the show's episodes—out of a total of 180—are the only two in which the character Kramer does not appear?

The Chinese Restaurant and ***The Pen***

Pot Luck
QUESTIONS

1. Which Canadian-born *Baywatch* star starred in *Home Improvements* as Lisa, in the show-within-a-show segment known as *Tool Time*?

2. Who voices the eldest of the Simpson family's children, Bart, in *The Simpsons*?

3. What are the names of the titular character's two aunts in *Sabrina the Teenage Witch*?

4. What is the name of the fictional character, played by Lucy Lawless, who first appeared in *Hercules: The Legendary Journeys*, and later returned in an eponymous 1995 to 1999 live-action series?

5. Which sitcom centers around a new arrival to the Banks family, whose children include Carlton and Hilary?

6. Which actor who starred in *That 70's Show* also voices the role of Meg Griffin in *Family Guy*?

7. Which *Star Trek* series, originally aired from 1987 to 1994, was set on the spaceship *USS Enterprise*?

1. Which Canadian-born *Baywatch* star starred in *Home Improvements* as Lisa, in the show-within-a-show segment known as *Tool Time*?

Pamela Anderson

In her first TV role, Anderson played the part of Tim's Tool Girl for the first two seasons of Home Improvement. *She later left due to scheduling conflicts with* Baywatch, *in which she became one of the longest-serving cast members by appearing from 1992 through until 1997.*

2. Who voices the eldest of the Simpson family's children, Bart, in *The Simpsons*?

Nancy Cartwright

3. What are the names of the titular character's two aunts in *Sabrina the Teenage Witch*?

Hilda and Zelda

4. What is the name of the fictional character, played by Lucy Lawless, who first appeared in *Hercules: The Legendary Journeys*, and later returned in an eponymous 1995 to 1999 live-action series?

Xena the Warrior Princess

5. Which sitcom centers around a new arrival to the Banks family, whose children include Carlton and Hilary?

The Fresh Prince of Bel-Air

6. Which actor who starred in *That 70's Show* also voices the role of Meg Griffin in *Family Guy*?

Mila Kunis

7. Which *Star Trek* series, originally aired from 1987 to 1994, was set on the spaceship *USS Enterprise*?

Star Trek: The Next Generation

Friends 2
QUESTIONS

1. Which band performed the famous *Friends* theme tune, *I'll Be There for You*?

2. In which US state was the show's title sequence filmed, showing the six protagonists dancing in a fountain surrounded by townhouses?

3. In the third episode of the first season, what does Phoebe find inside her can of soda, resulting in her receiving a large amount of compensation?

4. What is Chandler Bing's middle name?

5. Which guest star played the character of Richard Burke, a recurring love interest for Monica Geller who was 21 years her senior?

6. Which of these is not the title of a *Friends* episode?

   a. The One with the East German Laundry Detergent
   b. The One with the Tiny T-Shirt
   c. The One with the Photocopier Girl
   d. The One Where the Evil Monkey Gets Away

7. Unjumble the letters below to reveal the name of the character played by Joey Tribbiani on the fictionalized version of *Days of Our Lives*:

   ODD REMARK ARRAY
   (2, 5, 7)

1 Which band performed the famous *Friends* theme tune, *I'll Be There for You*?

The Rembrandts

After R.E.M. refused an offer to have their song Shiny Happy People *become the show's theme tune,* I'll Be There for You *was co-written by the show's creators, Marta Kauffman and David Crane, along with others, and The Rembrandts were drafted in by Warner Bros. to perform the now-iconic title track. It became so popular that the band eventually added additional verses and re-recorded it as a single, with the cast of* Friends *appearing in the accompanying music video.*

2 In which US state was the show's title sequence filmed, showing the six protagonists dancing in a fountain surrounded by townhouses?

California, at the Warner Bros. Studio

3 In the third episode of the first season, what does Phoebe find inside her can of soda, resulting in her receiving a large amount of compensation?

A human thumb

4 What is Chandler Bing's middle name?

Muriel

5 Which guest star played the character of Richard Burke, a recurring love interest for Monica Geller who was 21 years her senior?

Tom Selleck

6 Which of these is not the title of a *Friends* episode?

The One with the Photocopier Girl

7 Unjumble the letters below to reveal the name of the character played by Joey Tribbiani on the fictionalized version of *Days of Our Lives*:

ODD REMARK ARRAY (2, 5, 7)

Dr. Drake Ramoray

Sitcoms 2
QUESTIONS

1. In *Home Improvement*, Tim Allen's character is a passionate support of which Detroit football team?

2. In the final episode of *Full House*, which character, played by a pair of twins, suffers from a case of amnesia, causing her to briefly forget her entire family?

3. Which actor, who later won Best Actress Oscar for her role in *As Good as It Gets*, played the wife of Paul Reiser's character in the New York-based *Mad About You*?

4. In British sitcom *Keeping Up Appearances*, what is the spelling of main character Hyacinth's surname, which she insists should be pronounced "bouquet"?

5. Which iconic New York City river landmark lent its name to a sitcom which premiered in 1991, starring Marion Ross?

6. What is the name of the fictional news magazine which employs the eponymous lead character in *Murphy Brown*?

7. In the British sitcom of the same name created by Richard Curtis and Rowan Atkinson, what color is Mr. Bean's tie?

1 In *Home Improvement*, Tim Allen's character is a passionate support of which Detroit football team?

The Detroit Lions

> *Tim—the character played by Allen—is frequently presented as a sports fan, supporting his local teams. Alongside the Lions, he regularly wears clothing showing his love for the Pistons (basketball), Red Wings (hockey) and Tigers (baseball), all of which hail from Detroit.*

2 In the final episode of *Full House*, which character, played by a pair of twins, suffers from a case of amnesia, causing her to briefly forget her entire family?

Michelle Tanner

3 Which actor, who later won Best Actress Oscar for her role in *As Good as It Gets*, played the wife of Paul Reiser's character in the New York-based *Mad About You*?

Helen Hunt

4 In British sitcom *Keeping Up Appearances*, what is the spelling of main character Hyacinth's surname, which she insists should be pronounced "bouquet"?

Bucket

5 Which iconic New York City river landmark lent its name to a sitcom which premiered in 1991, starring Marion Ross?

Brooklyn Bridge

6 What is the name of the fictional news magazine which employs the eponymous lead character in *Murphy Brown*?

FYI

7 In the British sitcom of the same name created by Richard Curtis and Rowan Atkinson, what color is Mr. Bean's tie?

Red

Kids' Cartoons 2
QUESTIONS

1 What is the name of the elementary-school teacher who drives The Magic School Bus, in the show of the same name?

2 Change one letter in each word below to reveal the name of the spin-off of *The Rugrats*, which showed the cartoon's characters several years after the events of the original series?

AIL BROWN OP

3 Which one of these characters is the odd one out, being the only role not voiced by Christine Cavanaugh?

a. *Sonic the Hedgehog*'s Bunnie Rabbot
b. *Arthur*'s sister D.W.
c. Dexter, in *Dexter's Laboratory*
d. *The Rugrats*' Chuckie Finster

4 Which iconic musician, associated with the city of Memphis, was the titular character in *Johnny Bravo* based upon?

5 In the city-based cartoon *Hey Arnold!*, what is the name of Arnold's best friend, who usually wears a red shirt bearing the number 33?

6 Which of the main characters from schoolyard comedy *Recess* is usually known only by his initials?

7 In the animated series *Doug*, what is the name of the title character's bull terrier dog?

Kids' Cartoons 2

ANSWERS

1 What is the name of the elementary-school teacher who drives The Magic School Bus, in the show of the same name?

Miss Frizzle

Often called "The Friz" by her students, Valerie Frizzle is perhaps most recognizable for her red hair and flamboyant dress sense. Voiced by Lily Tomlin in this animated series, she is accompanied on wild and wonderful school trips by the class chameleon Liz, who occasionally also drives the bus.

2 Change one letter in each word below to reveal the name of the spin-off of *The Rugrats*, which showed the cartoon's characters several years after the events of the original series?

AIL BROWN OP

All Grown Up

3 Which one of these characters is the odd one out, being the only role not voiced by Christine Cavanaugh?

a. *Sonic the Hedgehog*'s Bunnie Rabbot
b. *Arthur*'s sister D.W.
c. Dexter, in *Dexter's Laboratory*
d. *The Rugrats*' Chuckie Finster

b. *Arthur*'s sister D.W.

4 Which iconic musician, associated with the city of Memphis, was the titular character in *Johnny Bravo* based upon?

Elvis Presley

5 In the city-based cartoon *Hey Arnold!*, what is the name of Arnold's best friend, who usually wears a red shirt bearing the number 33?

Gerald Johanssen

6 Which of the main characters from schoolyard comedy *Recess* is usually known only by his initials?

T.J.—short for Theodore Jasper

7 In the animated series *Doug*, what is the name of the title character's bull terrier dog?

Porkchop

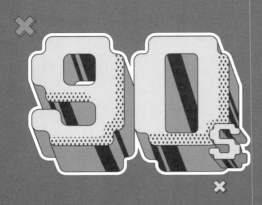

MUSIC

A time of boy bands with synchronized dancing and floppy hair, bubble-gum pop divas, plaid-clad grungers, and baggy-jeaned hip-hop breaking through—the 90s was a melting pot of sounds and styles that is often known as "the decade that doesn't fit." Throw in some G-funk, Britpop, reggae, thrash metal, techno, and dance-pop and you can see why the average 90s mixed tape was one of the most diverse going around.

You'll be Torn as You Oughta Know the answers, but let's see what happens when it reaches the round's Closing Time!

Boy Bands
QUESTIONS

1 What song, whose title begins with three repeated letters, was a major hit for the band Hanson in 1997?

2 *Step by Step* was the title of a hit single and album for which band, sometimes known by their initials NKOTB?

3 Which band had a 1997 hit with the song *As Long as You Love Me*?

4 While also being from a comment from Justin Timberlake's mother on how "in sync" the members' voices were, what is the significance of the letters forming the band name "*NSYNC"?

5 Aside from Robbie Williams, name two of the other four original Take That band members.

6 For how many consecutive weeks did Boyz II Men's 1992 single *End of the Road* stay at the top of the Billboard Hot 100?

a. 9
b. 13
c. 21
d. 44

7 Which ABBA track was covered by Irish band Westlife in 1999, peaking at number one hit in the UK charts, and was released as a double A-side along with *Seasons in the Sun*?

Boy Bands
ANSWERS

1 What song, whose title begins with three repeated letters, was a major hit for the band Hanson in 1997?

MMMBop

> *Having come a long way since the 90s, the Hanson brothers Isaac, Taylor, and Zac are all married and as of the start of 2022 have a whopping 15 kids between them. They also co-own a beer company offering a pale ale aptly called "Mmmhops".*

2 *Step by Step* was the title of a hit single and album for which band, sometimes known by their initials NKOTB?

New Kids on the Block

3 Which band had a 1997 hit with the song *As Long as You Love Me*?

Backstreet Boys

4 While also being from a comment from Justin Timberlake's mother on how "in sync" the members' voices were, what is the significance of the letters forming the band name "*NSYNC"?

The acronym is formed from the last letter of each of the initial members' first names: JustiN, ChriS, JoeY, JasoN, and JC

5 Aside from Robbie Williams, name two of the other four original Take That band members

Gary Barlow, Mark Owen, Jason Orange, or Howard Donald

6 For how many consecutive weeks did Boyz II Men's 1992 single *End of the Road* stay at the top of the Billboard Hot 100?

b. 13

7 Which ABBA track was covered by Irish band Westlife in 1999, peaking at number one hit in the UK charts, and was released as a double A-side along with *Seasons in the Sun*?

I Have a Dream

Grunge, Rock, & Punk 1

QUESTIONS

1 With which US city is the grunge genre most associated, thanks to its thriving independent music scene and the influential record label Sub Pop?

2 What is the title of British band Radiohead's third album, released in 1997 and featuring the single *No Surprises*?

3 Why did rock band Alice in Chains find themselves homeless on returning home to Seattle after their 1993 Lollapalooza tour?

4 From which 1999 Red Hot Chili Peppers album were the songs *Scar Tissue* and *Otherside* released as singles, along with the album's title track?

5 Which punk-rock band had a hit with the song *All the Small Things* from their 1999 album, *Enema of the State*, featuring a chorus with the lyrics "Say it ain't so, I will not go"?

6 What is the title of Nirvana's second album, which features the tracks *Come as You Are* and *Smells Like Teen Spirit*?

7 Rearrange the following letters to find the name of a popular 90s band:

MAPLE JAR (5, 3)

Grunge, Rock, & Punk 1
ANSWERS

1 With which US city is the grunge genre most associated, thanks to its thriving independent music scene and the influential record label Sub Pop?

Seattle

Grunge is sometimes known as the "Seattle sound", and fuses elements of both metal and punk. The independent label Sub Pop used "grunge" as a marketing term for the music, and it soon started to spread in popularity. Bands such as Nirvana and Pearl Jam had major hits with grunge tracks.

2 What is the title of British band Radiohead's third album, released in 1997 and featuring the single *No Surprises*?

OK Computer

3 Why did rock band Alice in Chains find themselves homeless on returning home to Seattle after their 1993 Lollapalooza tour?

They had been evicted after not paying their rent

4 From which 1999 Red Hot Chili Peppers album were the songs *Scar Tissue* and *Otherside* released as singles, along with the album's title track?

Californication

5 Which punk-rock band had a hit with the song *All the Small Things* from their 1999 album, *Enema of the State*, featuring a chorus with the lyrics "Say it ain't so, I will not go"?

blink-182

6 What is the title of Nirvana's second album, which features the tracks *Come as You Are* and *Smells Like Teen Spirit*?

Nevermind

7 Rearrange the following letters to find the name of a popular 90s band:

MAPLE JAR (5, 3)

Pearl Jam

Complete the Lyrics 1
QUESTIONS

Fill in the words missing from each set of lyrics.

1 Nirvana, *Smells Like Teen Spirit*:

"Here we are now, entertain us
I feel _____ and _____"

2 Robbie Williams, *Angels*:

"And through it all
She offers me _____"

3 Backstreet Boys, *I Want It That Way*:

"You are my _____
The one _____"

4 Britney Spears, *... Baby One More Time*:

"My _____ is killing me"

5 Spice Girls, *Wannabe*:

"Make it last forever
_____ never ends"

6 Green Day, *Good Riddance (Time of your Life)*:

"Another turning point
A _____ stuck in the road"

7 Celine Dion, *My Heart Will Go On*:

"Every night in my dreams
I _____ you, I _____
you"

Complete the Lyrics 1
ANSWERS

Fill in the words missing from each set of lyrics.

1 Nirvana, *Smells Like Teen Spirit*:

"Here we are now, entertain us
I feel _____ and _____"

Stupid; contagious

> Smells Like Teen Spirit *was the lead single from Nirvana's second album, Nevermind, and was written by Kurt Cobain. It was the band's most successful track in many countries, but the band eventually grew uncomfortable with this success and excluded it from later performances. Cobain said it was "almost an embarrassment to play it" due to its unusual success.*

2 Robbie Williams, *Angels*:

"And through it all
She offers me _____"

Protection

3 Backstreet Boys, *I Want It That Way*:

"You are my _____
The one _____"

Fire; desire

4 Britney Spears, *... Baby One More Time*:

"My _____ is killing me"

Loneliness

5 Spice Girls, *Wannabe*:

"Make it last forever
_____ never ends"

Friendship

6 Green Day, *Good Riddance (Time of your Life)*:

"Another turning point
A _____ stuck in the road"

Fork

7 Celine Dion, *My Heart Will Go On*:

"Every night in my dreams
I _____ you, I _____ you"

See; feel

Number Ones
QUESTIONS

1 Which hip-hop duo was known for the 1992 chart-topping song and its film clip in which they wore their pants back-to-front?

2 Change one letter in each word below to reveal the title of a Technotronic song included in the 1990 Billboard Year-End Hot 100?

PULP US TOE RAM

3 Which Cher song reached the top of the Billboard Hot 100 in 1999, 33 years after her previous number one US hit?

4 What is the title of the Meat Loaf song released in 1993 which was the best-selling single that year in the UK, spending seven weeks at the top of the UK charts?

5 Name the title and artist of the ballad that was recorded for the film *Four Weddings and a Funeral*, which then spent 15 consecutive weeks at number one in the UK charts.

6 What is the title of Jennifer Lopez's debut single, which spent five weeks on top of the Billboard Hot 100 in 1999?

7 Who wrote and released *Truly Madly Deeply* in 1997, which topped the US Billboard Hot 100 and reached number four in the UK?

Number Ones
ANSWERS

1 Which hip-hop duo was known for the 1992 chart-topping song and its film clip in which they wore their pants back-to-front?

Kris Kross

The two members of Kris Kross, Chris Kelly and Chris Smith, were only 12 and 13 years old when their first album Totally Crossed Out went platinum. Jump was also the first rap song to ever top the Billboard Hot 100 chart for eight weeks.

2 Change one letter in each word below to reveal the title of a Technotronic song included in the 1990 Billboard Year-End Hot 100?

PULP US TOE RAM

Pump Up the Jam

3 Which Cher song reached the top of the Billboard Hot 100 in 1999, 33 years after her previous number one US hit?

Believe

4 What is the title of the Meat Loaf song released in 1993 which was the best-selling single that year in the UK, spending seven weeks at the top of the UK charts?

I'd Do Anything for Love (But I Won't Do That)

5 Name the title and artist of the ballad that was recorded for the film *Four Weddings and a Funeral*, which then spent 15 consecutive weeks at number one in the UK charts.

Love is All Around by Wet Wet Wet

6 What is the title of Jennifer Lopez's debut single, which spent five weeks on top of the Billboard Hot 100 in 1999?

If You Had My Love

7 Who wrote and released *Truly Madly Deeply* in 1997, which topped the US Billboard Hot 100 and reached number four in the UK?

Savage Garden

Music Videos

1 The debut music video for which singer and former Disney Mouseketeer was filmed in the same high school as the 1978 movie *Grease*?

2 What Lenny Kravitz song sung from the point of view of Jesus won Best Male Video at the MTV VMAs?

3 Which song by Queen was featured in the film *Wayne's World*, prompting the release of a new music video which subsequently won Best Video from a Film at the VMAs?

4 The video for which Supergrass song showed the band attempting to play their instruments as puppets with extremely long arms and legs?

5 What is the title of the song for whose music video Weezer recreated an episode of the classic TV show *Happy Days*?

6 For which 1999 song did Ricky Martin win the VMA for Best Dance Video and again for Best Pop Video?

7 Which British funk band won Video of the Year at the MTV Video Music Awards with their track *Virtual Insanity*?

Music Videos
ANSWERS

1 The debut music video for which singer and former Disney Mouseketeer was filmed in the same high school as the 1978 movie *Grease*?

Britney Spears

The video was for …Baby One More Time, a song which topped the charts in over twenty countries and which was in 2020 named by Rolling Stone as the greatest debut single of all time. The video itself was subsequently voted best video of the 1990s in a Billboard poll.

2 What Lenny Kravitz song sung from the point of view of Jesus won Best Male Video at the MTV VMAs?

Are You Gonna Go My Way

3 Which song by Queen was featured in the film *Wayne's World*, prompting the release of a new music video which subsequently won Best Video from a Film at the VMAs?

Bohemian Rhapsody

4 The video for which Supergrass song showed the band attempting to play their instruments as puppets with extremely long arms and legs?

Pumping on Your Stereo

5 What is the title of the song for whose music video Weezer recreated an episode of the classic TV show *Happy Days*?

Buddy Holly

6 For which 1999 song did Ricky Martin win the VMA for Best Dance Video and again for Best Pop Video?

Livin' La Vida Loca

7 Which British funk band won Video of the Year at the MTV Video Music Awards with their track *Virtual Insanity*?

Jamiroquai

One-hit Wonders 1
QUESTIONS

1 Which song by Los Del Rio, remixed by The Bayside Boys, includes sections in both English and Spanish and went on to spawn a well-known international dance?

2 Which song by Deep Blue Something references a film of the same name in its lyrics, which featured Audrey Hepburn in the role of Holly Golightly?

3 Change one letter in each word below to reveal the name of a 1994 song which featured in the films *Matilda* and *Ice Age*:

SAND HE OR BY WHY

4 Which 1999 hit by Lou Bega sampled a song of largely the same name, originally recorded by Cuban musician Dámaso Pérez Prado in 1949?

5 What is the title of the hit 1991 song by Marc Cohn which was inspired by various locations in Tennessee, including Elvis Presley's former home?

6 Which band released the song *Steal My Sunshine*, which opens with the lyric "I was lying on the grass on Sunday morning of last week"?

7 What is the only letter to appear in the title of the 1993 hit by Crash Test Dummies which opens with the lyric "Once there was this kid who / Got into an accident"?

One-hit Wonders 1

ANSWERS

1 Which song by Los Del Rio, remixed by The Bayside Boys, includes sections in both English and Spanish and went on to spawn a well-known international dance?

Macarena

> *The song is named after the daughter of one half of the Los Del Rio duo, and did not become a worldwide hit until the Bayside Boys created a remix of the song that added in English lyrics and a dance beat. The subsequent version remained at number one on the Billboard Hot 100 for fourteen weeks.*

2 Which song by Deep Blue Something references a film of the same name in its lyrics, which featured Audrey Hepburn in the role of Holly Golightly?

Breakfast at Tiffany's

3 Change one letter in each word below to reveal the name of a 1994 song which featured in the films *Matilda* and *Ice Age*:

SAND HE OR BY WHY

Send Me on My Way

4 Which 1999 hit by Lou Bega sampled a song of largely the same name, originally recorded by Cuban musician Dámaso Pérez Prado in 1949?

Mambo No. 5 (A Little Bit Of...)

5 What is the title of the hit 1991 song by Marc Cohn which was inspired by various locations in Tennessee, including Elvis Presley's former home?

Walking in Memphis

6 Which band released the song *Steal My Sunshine*, which opens with the lyric "I was lying on the grass on Sunday morning of last week"?

Len

7 What is the only letter to appear in the title of the 1993 hit by Crash Test Dummies which opens with the lyric "Once there was this kid who / Got into an accident"?

M, in *Mmm Mmm Mmm Mmm*

Pot Luck 1
QUESTIONS

1 Which song, originally released by the band Wild Cherry in 1976, was covered by Vanilla Ice in 1990?

2 Which song, written and recorded by Sir Mix-a-Lot, was accompanied by a music video that was briefly banned by MTV?

3 Which 1991 ballad by Extreme marked a departure from their usual rock metal style, but reached number one on the Billboard Hot 100?

4 Which 1990 single by Wilson Phillips won the Billboard Music Award for Hot 100 Single of the Year?

5 Roxette's *It Must Have Been Love* featured in which 1990 film soundtrack?

6 Which hip-hop duo released *Summertime* in 1991, winning them a Grammy for Best Rap Performance by a Duo or Group?

7 What is the one-word title of the song by CeCe Peniston which was released as her debut single in 1991, reaching both number five on the Billboard Hot 100 and number two in the UK chart?

Pot Luck 1
ANSWERS

1 Which song, originally released by the band Wild Cherry in 1976, was covered by Vanilla Ice in 1990?

Play That Funky Music

The single's B-side, Ice Ice Baby, was such a success that the song was later released a year later, charting in its own right.

2 Which song, written and recorded by Sir Mix-a-Lot, was accompanied by a music video that was briefly banned by MTV?

Baby Got Back

3 Which 1991 ballad by Extreme marked a departure from their usual rock metal style, but reached number one on the Billboard Hot 100?

More Than Words

4 Which 1990 single by Wilson Phillips won the Billboard Music Award for Hot 100 Single of the Year?

Hold On

5 Roxette's *It Must Have Been Love* featured in which 1990 film soundtrack?

Pretty Woman

6 Which hip-hop duo released Summertime in 1991, winning them a Grammy for Best Rap Performance by a Duo or Group?

DJ Jazzy Jeff & The Fresh Prince

7 What is the one-word title of the song by CeCe Peniston which was released as her debut single in 1991, reaching both number five on the Billboard Hot 100 and number two in the UK chart?

Finally

Rap & Hip Hop 1
QUESTIONS

1 Which hip hop group, formed in the early 1990s, consists of Wyclef Jean, Pras Michel and Lauryn Hill?

2 Which rapper released their debut album *Supa Dupa Fly* in 1997, which was produced by Timbaland and recorded in just two weeks?

3 Which US rapper's real name is Calvin Cordozar Broadus Jr.? He appeared with Dr. Dre on the 1999 single *Still D.R.E.*

4 Which artist released *The Slim Shady LP* in 1999, featuring the track *My Name Is*?

5 Rearrange the letters below to create the name of Jay-Z's 1996 debut album:

ELABORATE BOUNDS (10, 5)

6 What is the title of the 1996 single by Blackstreet which features an initial verse rapped by Dr. Dre, and the repeated refrain "I like the way you work it"?

7 Which Tupac Shakur song, with a two-word alliterative title, was recorded in 1992 but released posthumously on a 2004 album and 2005 single that feature vocal samples from a 1971 Elton John song?

Rap & Hip Hop 1

ANSWERS

1 Which hip hop group, formed in the early 1990s, consists of Wyclef Jean, Pras Michel and Lauryn Hill?

(The) Fugees

The name "Fugees" came from a shortening of "refugees", and their second album, The Score (1996), is one of the most successful albums of all time, having sold around 22 million copies. Pras Michel and Lauryn Hill met at school in New Jersey, while Wyclef Jean is Pras's cousin.

2 Which rapper released their debut album *Supa Dupa Fly* in 1997, which was produced by Timbaland and recorded in just two weeks?

Missy Elliott

3 Which US rapper's real name is Calvin Cordozar Broadus Jr.? He appeared with Dr. Dre on the 1999 single *Still D.R.E.*

Snoop Dogg

4 Which artist released *The Slim Shady LP* in 1999, featuring the track *My Name Is*?

Eminem

5 Rearrange the letters below to create the name of Jay-Z's 1996 debut album:

ELABORATE BOUNDS (10, 5)

Reasonable Doubt

6 What is the title of the 1996 single by Blackstreet which features an initial verse rapped by Dr. Dre, and the repeated refrain "I like the way you work it"?

No Diggity

7 Which Tupac Shakur song, with a two-word alliterative title, was recorded in 1992 but released posthumously on a 2004 album and 2005 single that feature vocal samples from a 1971 Elton John song?

Ghetto Gospel

Solo Legends 1
QUESTIONS

1 With which singer-songwriter did George Michael duet on the 1991 release, *Don't Let the Sun Go Down on Me*?

2 For which 1996 film starring Robert Redford and Michelle Pfeiffer did Celine Dion record the song *Because You Loved Me*?

3 What is the one-word title of Mariah Carey's second album, released in 1991, from which she released a number-one single of the same name?

4 Rearrange the letters below to reveal the title of a 1993 film starring Janet Jackson, for which she performed and co-wrote the track *Again*, which earned an Academy Award nomination?

SET TOPIC JUICE (6, 7)

5 Which 1990 song by George Michael had the number "90" added to the end of its title, in an attempt to avoid confusion with a track of the same name which had been previously recorded by Wham! in 1984?

6 On which 1999 track can Whitney Houston's daughter be heard saying "Sing, mommy", after the opening lyric of "If tomorrow is judgment day"?

7 For which 1996 film did Madonna record the song *You Must Love Me*, which did not feature in the original show on which the movie was based?

Solo Legends 1
ANSWERS

1 With which singer-songwriter did George Michael duet on the 1991 release, *Don't Let the Sun Go Down on Me?*

Elton John

The song was originally released in 1974 both on Elton John's album Caribou and as a single that reached number two in the Billboard Hot 100 chart, but it had to wait until the 1991 version to achieve number one in the chart—a feat which it also achieved in the UK singles chart too—although he and George Michael had in fact first performed the song as a duet during the Live Aid concert in 1985.

2 For which 1996 film starring Robert Redford and Michelle Pfeiffer did Celine Dion record the song *Because You Loved Me?*

Up Close & Personal

3 What is the one-word title of Mariah Carey's second album, released in 1991, from which she released a number-one single of the same name?

Emotions

4 Rearrange the letters below to reveal the title of a 1993 film starring Janet Jackson, for which she performed and co-wrote the track *Again*, which earned an Academy Award nomination?

SET TOPIC JUICE (6, 7)

Poetic Justice

5 Which 1990 song by George Michael had the number "90" added to the end of its title, in an attempt to avoid confusion with a track of the same name which had been previously recorded by Wham! in 1984?

Freedom! 90

6 On which 1999 track can Whitney Houston's daughter be heard saying "Sing, mommy", after the opening lyric of "If tomorrow is judgment day"?

My Love is Your Love

7 For which 1996 film did Madonna record the song *You Must Love Me*, which did not feature in the original show on which the movie was based?

Evita

Britpop
QUESTIONS

1. A member of which British band said about his brother, "He's the angriest man you'll ever meet. He's like a man with a fork in a world of soup."?

2. Which song by Blur opens with the lyric "Confidence is a preference for the habitual voyeur"?

3. Which singer and songwriter, born in East London, is the frontman for the band Blur?

4. Which band released the double A-side single *Alright / Should Coco* in 1995, and which also featured on the soundtrack to the movie *Clueless*?

5. Which band, named after a type of fabric, released the single *Animal Nitrate* from their self-titled debut album in 1993?

6. Complete the quote from Oasis member Liam Gallagher, "We'd rather play in front of 200 Oasis fans than 60,000 _____ fans."
   a. Britney Spears
   b. Death Metal
   c. The Wiggles
   d. Blur

7. Which band, started by 15-year-old Jarvis Cocker in 1978, saw Jarvis jump off a monitor, slip in a puddle, and fall flat on his back after their 1995 hit went to number two in the charts?

1 A member of which British band said about his brother, "He's the angriest man you'll ever meet. He's like a man with a fork in a world of soup."?

***Oasis*—Noel Gallagher about his brother, Liam Gallagher**

> In 2009 the band finally split, with Noel Gallagher saying of his brother, "It's with some sadness and great relief to tell you that I quit Oasis tonight. People will write and say what they like, but I simply could not go on working with Liam a day longer."

2 Which song by Blur opens with the lyric "Confidence is a preference for the habitual voyeur"?

Parklife

3 Which singer and songwriter, born in East London, is the frontman for the band Blur?

Damon Albarn

4 Which band released the double A-side single *Alright / Should Coco* in 1995, and which also featured on the soundtrack to the movie *Clueless*?

Supergrass

5 Which band, named after a type of fabric, released the single *Animal Nitrate* from their self-titled debut album in 1993?

Suede

6 Complete the quote from Oasis member Liam Gallagher, "We'd rather play in front of 200 Oasis fans than 60,000 _____ fans."

a. Britney Spears
b. Death Metal
c. The Wiggles
d. Blur

b. Death Metal

7 Which band, started by 15-year-old Jarvis Cocker in 1978, saw Jarvis jump off a monitor, slip in a puddle, and fall flat on his back after their 1995 hit went to number two in the charts?

Pulp—for *Common People*

R&B 1
QUESTIONS

1 Which band became the inaugural winner of the Grammy for Best R&B Album after releasing *II*, which included the hit single *I'll Make Love to You*?

2 *What's the 411?* and *My Life* are both albums, released in 1992 and 1994 respectively, from which American singer?

3 *Say My Name*, *Bills, Bills, Bills*, and *Jumpin' Jumpin'* are all tracks from which 1999 album by Destiny's Child?

4 Which one of the two singers who joined Destiny's Child in 1999 remained to see success as a three-piece with their 2000 single, *Independent Women Part 1*, which was included on the *Charlie's Angels* movie soundtrack?

5 Which 1998 duet by singers Brandy and Monica, inspired by a similarly named song by Michael Jackson, won the Grammy Award for Best R&B Vocal Performance by a Duo or Group?

6 What was the name of the 1999 TLC song that was named after a six-letter slang term for "insignificant or contemptible people"?

7 Which 1999 track, produced by The Neptunes and recorded by Kelis, features the sung-shouted line "I hate you so much right now" in the chorus?

1 Which band became the inaugural winner of the Grammy for Best R&B Album after releasing *II*, which included the hit single *I'll Make Love to You*?

Boyz II Men

The album was Boyz II Men's third studio album, and included not only I'll Make Love to You but also On Bended Knee, both of which were consecutive number one hits on the Billboard Hot 100, marking only the third time that an artist had knocked themselves off the number one position in the chart. The only previous artists to have achieved this were The Beatles and Elvis.

2 *What's the 411?* and *My Life* are both albums, released in 1992 and 1994 respectively, from which American singer?

Mary J. Blige

3 *Say My Name*, *Bills, Bills, Bills*, and *Jumpin' Jumpin'* are all tracks from which 1999 album by Destiny's Child?

The Writing's on the Wall

4 Which one of the two singers who joined Destiny's Child in 1999 remained to see success as a three-piece with their 2000 single, *Independent Women Part 1*, which was included on the *Charlie's Angels* movie soundtrack?

Michelle Williams

5 Which 1998 duet by singers Brandy and Monica, inspired by a similarly named song by Michael Jackson, won the Grammy Award for Best R&B Vocal Performance by a Duo or Group?

The Boy Is Mine

6 What was the name of the 1999 TLC song that was named after a six-letter slang term for "insignificant or contemptible people"?

No Scrubs

7 Which 1999 track, produced by The Neptunes and recorded by Kelis, features the sung-shouted line "I hate you so much right now" in the chorus?

Caught Out There

Singer-Songwriters 1
QUESTIONS

1 Which Canadian–American artist released their third album, *Jagged Little Pill*, in 1995?

2 Which Australian singer-songwriter achieved international success with a cover of the song *Torn*, released in 1997?

3 Which artist released their debut album *Tidal* in 1996, from which the single *Criminal* earned them a Grammy Award?

4 What is the name of Shania Twain's third studio album, from which the tracks *You're Still the One* and *Man! I Feel Like a Woman!* were released—alongside a staggering ten other singles?

5 Which iconic 1995 song from Icelandic musician Björk is in fact a cover of a 1951 B-side release by Betty Hutton, which itself was a cover of a 1948 German song, *Und jetzt ist es still*?

6 Jewel's debut album was released in which year?

a. 1990
b. 1993
c. 1995
d. 1997

7 What is the title of the Grammy-award-winning song by Sheryl Crow that is based on the poem *Fun* by Wyn Cooper? The song's title is also the first line of the poem that inspired it.

Singer-Songwriters 1

ANSWERS

1 Which Canadian–American artist released their third album, *Jagged Little Pill*, in 1995?

Alanis Morrissette

> *Jagged Little Pill was Morrissette's first international album release. The album's first single,* You Oughta Know, *won acclaim for its scathing lyrics about a former relationship and "the liberation that comes from speaking the truth", but it was the fourth single from the album,* Ironic, *that became her biggest hit.*

2 Which Australian singer-songwriter achieved international success with a cover of the song *Torn*, released in 1997?

Natalie Imbruglia

3 Which artist released their debut album *Tidal* in 1996, from which the single *Criminal* earned them a Grammy Award?

Fiona Apple

4 What is the name of Shania Twain's third studio album, from which the tracks *You're Still the One* and *Man! I Feel Like a Woman!* were released—alongside a staggering ten other singles?

Come On Over

5 Which iconic 1995 song from Icelandic musician Björk is in fact a cover of a 1951 B-side release by Betty Hutton, which itself was a cover of a 1948 German song, *Und jetzt ist es still*?

It's Oh So Quiet

6 Jewel's debut album was released in which year?

a. 1990
b. 1993
c. 1995
d. 1997

c. 1995

7 What is the title of the Grammy-award-winning song by Sheryl Crow that is based on the poem *Fun* by Wyn Cooper? The song's title is also the first line of the poem that inspired it.

All I Wanna Do

The Spice Girls
QUESTIONS

1 What was the name of the Spice Girls's debut single, released in 1996?

2 Which performer, who won a Best Actress Oscar in 2016, partly chose her professional name to match one of the band members' given names?

3 During which 1997 musical awards show did Geri Halliwell wear a now-iconic dress with a Union Jack design?

4 Who was the final Spice Girl to join the five-piece line-up, becoming their youngest member?

5 What was the one-word title of the group's second album, which has been anagrammed below?

CROWD SPIEL

6 In the band's 1997 movie, in which the five Spice Girls play fictionalized versions of themselves, which Eswatini-born actor played the group's manager?

7 What was the original name of the band the group members were selected for, before eventually becoming the Spice Girls?

a. Touch
b. Crash
c. Secrets
d. Smash

The Spice Girls
ANSWERS

1 What was the name of the Spice Girls's debut single, released in 1996?

Wannabe

> *Reportedly recorded in under an hour, the song features solo performances from all of the Spice Girls except (as-then) Victoria Adams, a.k.a. 'Posh Spice' and later Victoria Beckham. The footsteps which can be heard at the beginning of the recording are those of Mel B, running up towards the microphone. The song topped the charts, certifying three-times platinum in the UK and two-times platinum in the US.*

2 Which performer, who won a Best Actress Oscar in 2016, partly chose her professional name to match one of the band members' given names?

Emma Stone

3 During which 1997 musical awards show did Geri Halliwell wear a now-iconic dress with a Union Jack design?

The BRIT Awards

4 Who was the final Spice Girl to join the five-piece line-up, becoming their youngest member?

Emma Bunton, a.k.a. "Baby Spice"

5 What was the one-word title of the group's second album, which has been anagrammed below?

CROWD SPIEL

Spiceworld

6 In the band's 1997 movie, in which the five Spice Girls play fictionalized versions of themselves, which Eswatini-born actor played the group's manager?

Richard E. Grant

7 What was the original name of the band the group members were selected for, before eventually becoming the Spice Girls?

a. Touch
b. Crash
c. Secrets
d. Smash

a. Touch

Grunge, Rock, & Punk 2
QUESTIONS

1 Which band with a vegetable-themed name released the album *Mellon Collie and the Infinite Sadness* in 1995?

2 Which alternative rock band won a Grammy award for their 1992 single, *Losing My Religion*?

3 Which singer was the frontwoman for the band Hole, who released the album *Live Through This* in 1994?

4 Although it was never released as a single, which Rage Against the Machine song garnered significant popularity after being included in the soundtrack of the movie *The Matrix*?

5 Delete one letter in each pair below to reveal the name of the 1994 album by Green Day which features the songs *Basket Case* and *When I Come Around*:

SD OE AO TK IT LE

6 Which band released the single *Don't Speak* in 1995, which was later nominated for Song of the Year at the Grammy Awards?

7 Which band formed by ex-Nirvana drummer Dave Grohl released the album *The Colour and the Shape* in 1997, as a follow-up to a previous self-titled debut album?

Grunge, Rock, & Punk 2

ANSWERS

1 Which band with a vegetable-themed name released the album *Mellon Collie and the Infinite Sadness* in 1995?

(The) Smashing Pumpkins

The name was made up by lead singer/songwriter Billy Corgan as a child, long before he formed the band, as a joke name of a band he was allegedly in. It was inspired by a prank he witnessed growing up in Illinois, where people took Halloween pumpkins from doorsteps and then smashed them to bits in the middle of the street.

2 Which alternative rock band won a Grammy award for their 1992 single, *Losing My Religion*?

R.E.M.

3 Which singer was the frontwoman for the band Hole, who released the album *Live Through This* in 1994?

Courtney Love

4 Although it was never released as a single, which Rage Against the Machine song garnered significant popularity after being included in the soundtrack of the movie *The Matrix*?

Wake Up

5 Delete one letter in each pair below to reveal the name of the 1994 album by Green Day which features the songs *Basket Case* and *When I Come Around*:

SD OE AO TK IT LE

Dookie

6 Which band released the single *Don't Speak* in 1995, which was later nominated for Song of the Year at the Grammy Awards?

No Doubt

7 Which band formed by ex-Nirvana drummer Dave Grohl released the album *The Colour and the Shape* in 1997, as a follow-up to a previous self-titled debut album?

Foo Fighters

One-hit Wonders 2
QUESTIONS

1. Which Danish band released a 1997 single which prompted ultimately unsuccessful legal action from toy manufacturers Mattel, who claimed the song violated their doll's trademark and tarnished its reputation?

2. Rearrange the following letters to restore the name of the band who released *No Rain* in 1993?

   NOBLE N MILD (5, 5)

3. For which 1993 song were the band Spin Doctors nominated for a Grammy Award for Best Rock Performance by a Duo or Group?

4. Which Sixpence None the Richer song featured heavily in the soundtrack to the 1999 teen romcom, *She's All That*?

5. From which song by Queen is the bassline of Vanilla Ice's *Ice, Ice Baby* sampled?

6. Which song by The La's featured in several films released in the 1990s, including *The Parent Trap*, *Fever Pitch*, and *Girl, Interrupted*?

7. Which song, released by Swedish group Rednex in 1994, has a chorus which features the question "Where did you come from / where did you go"?

One-hit Wonders 2

ANSWERS

1 Which Danish band released a 1997 single which prompted ultimately unsuccessful legal action from toy manufacturers Mattel, who claimed the song violated their doll's trademark and tarnished its reputation?

Aqua

> *The song, Barbie Girl, was a worldwide success, particularly in Europe where it was later performed as part of an Aqua medley during the interval at the Eurovision Song Contest. Aqua subsequently had further hits, becoming the most profitable Danish band of all time, but Barbie Girl remains their most successful song.*

2 Rearrange the following letters to restore the name of the band who released *No Rain* in 1993?

NOBLE N MILD (5, 5)

Blind Melon

3 For which 1993 song were the band Spin Doctors nominated for a Grammy Award for Best Rock Performance by a Duo or Group?

Two Princes

4 Which Sixpence None the Richer song featured heavily in the soundtrack to the 1999 teen romcom, *She's All That*?

Kiss Me

5 From which song by Queen is the bassline of Vanilla Ice's *Ice, Ice Baby* sampled?

Under Pressure

6 Which song by The La's featured in several films released in the 1990s, including *The Parent Trap*, *Fever Pitch*, and *Girl, Interrupted*?

There She Goes

7 Which song, released by Swedish group Rednex in 1994, has a chorus which features the question "Where did you come from / where did you go"?

Cotton Eye Joe

Rap & Hip-Hop 2
QUESTIONS

1 Which single by rapper The Notorious B.I.G. was a posthumous hit when it was released in 1997, sampling Diana Ross's 1980 hit *I'm Coming Out*?

2 What is the name of the 1995 track by 2Pac which includes the name of a US state in its title, and which features vocals by Dr Dre and Roger Troutman?

3 Which song from the musical *Annie* was sampled on a similarly named 1998 Jay-Z track, going on to become one of the rapper's first hits?

4 What is the title of the only studio album released by Lauryn Hill, which is said to be the best-ever-selling album by a female rapper?

5 Which 1992 track by House of Pain opens with the lyrics "Pack it up, pack it in, let me begin"?

6 What is the real name of the rapper who, as Puff Daddy, released the song *I'll Be Missing You* in 1997, which sampled a song by the Police and honored his friend The Notorious B.I.G.?

7 The Salt-N-Pepa song *Whatta Man* also featured which other 90s girl band?

Rap & Hip-Hop 2
ANSWERS

1 Which single by rapper The Notorious B.I.G. was a posthumous hit when it was released in 1997, sampling Diana Ross's 1980 hit *I'm Coming Out*?

Mo Money Mo Problems

> *The song went to number one in the Billboard Hot 100 chart, repeating the feat of The Notorious B.I.G.'s previous (and first) posthumous hit, Hypnotize. Its video included archive footage of the rapper that had had its speed changed so that it seemed to match to the track's lyrics.*

2 What is the name of the 1995 track by 2Pac which includes the name of a US state in its title, and which features vocals by Dr Dre and Roger Troutman?

California Love

3 Which song from the musical *Annie* was sampled on a similarly named 1998 Jay-Z track, going on to become one of the rapper's first hits?

It's the Hard Knock Life

4 What is the title of the only studio album released by Lauryn Hill, which is said to be the best-ever-selling album by a female rapper?

The Miseducation of Lauryn Hill

5 Which 1992 track by House of Pain opens with the lyrics "Pack it up, pack it in, let me begin"?

Jump Around

6 What is the real name of the rapper who, as Puff Daddy, released the song *I'll Be Missing You* in 1997, which sampled a song by the Police and honored his friend The Notorious B.I.G.?

Sean Combs

7 The Salt-N-Pepa song *Whatta Man* also featured which other 90s girl band?

En Vogue

Pot Luck 2
QUESTIONS

1 Which British reggae band had a 1993 hit with a version of Elvis Presley's *Can't Help Falling in Love*?

2 Who wrote and recorded the 1994 song *The Most Beautiful Girl in the World*, which remains their only number one hit in the UK singles chart?

3 Which singer first released the reggae-inspired single *Mysterious Girl* in Australia, in 1995?

4 What is the title of the hit 1998 single by Shania Twain which mentions both Elvis and Brad Pitt in its lyrics?

5 *How Do I Live* was a hit single for which singer-songwriter, who originally found fame in the country music scene?

6 Which girl band released three of the top five best-selling singles in the UK in 1996?

7 Which artist had the most number-one hits on the Billboard Hot 100 in the 1990s, with a whopping 14?

1 Which British reggae band had a 1993 hit with a version of Elvis Presley's *Can't Help Falling in Love*?

UB40

> *Originally recorded by Presley for the album* Blue Hawaii, *the song has been covered by artists as diverse as Bob Dylan and A-Teens. The UB40 version spent seven weeks at the top of the Billboard Hot 100, and two weeks at the top of the UK chart.*

2 Who wrote and recorded the 1994 song *The Most Beautiful Girl in the World*, which remains their only number one hit in the UK singles chart?

Prince (although at the time he used the symbol ⚥ as his stage name, and was also known as The Artist Formerly Known As Prince)

3 Which singer first released the reggae-inspired single *Mysterious Girl* in Australia, in 1995?

Peter Andre

4 What is the title of the hit 1998 single by Shania Twain which mentions both Elvis and Brad Pitt in its lyrics?

That Don't Impress Me Much

5 *How Do I Live* was a hit single for which singer-songwriter, who originally found fame in the country music scene?

LeAnn Rimes

6 Which girl band released three of the top five best-selling singles in the UK in 1996?

Spice Girls

7 Which artist had the most number-one hits on the Billboard Hot 100 in the 1990s, with a whopping 14?

Mariah Carey

Teen Pop
QUESTIONS

1 Britney Spears's first studio album was …*Baby One More Time*, but what was the somewhat self-descriptive title of her second album?

2 Which two-word phrase, often used by the Spice Girls, became a popular symbol of female independence and empowerment in the 1990s?

3 Change one letter in each word below to reveal the title of a 1999 single by Britney Spears that also featured on her debut album:

BURN SO MALE YOB HARPY

4 Who released their debut single *Candy* in 1999 at the age of 15—a title which rhymes with their given name?

5 Which singer released a self-titled debut album in 1999, including the hits *Genie in a Bottle* and *What a Girl Wants*?

6 What is the name of the seven-piece British vocal group, put together by the former manager of the Spice Girls, which had a 1999 UK hit with the single *Bring It All Back*?

7 Which 1998 song with a French-language title was a number one hit in the UK for Irish girl band B*Witched, also reaching number nine on the US Billboard Hot 100?

1 Britney Spears's first studio album was ...*Baby One More Time*, but what was the somewhat self-descriptive title of her second album?

Oops!... I Did It Again

She did indeed do it again, with both of her first two albums achieving huge international success. Oops!... I Did It Again has sold more than 20 million copies, making it one of the most successful albums of all time, reaching number one in the US, UK, Australia, New Zealand and many other countries.

2 Which two-word phrase, often used by the Spice Girls, became a popular symbol of female independence and empowerment in the 1990s?

Girl Power

3 Change one letter in each word below to reveal the title of a 1999 single by Britney Spears that also featured on her debut album:

BURN SO MALE YOB HARPY

Born to Make You Happy

4 Who released their debut single *Candy* in 1999 at the age of 15—a title which rhymes with their given name?

Mandy Moore

5 Which singer released a self-titled debut album in 1999, including the hits *Genie in a Bottle* and *What a Girl Wants*?

Christina Aguilera

6 What is the name of the seven-piece British vocal group, put together by the former manager of the Spice Girls, which had a 1999 UK hit with the single *Bring It All Back*?

S Club 7

7 Which 1998 song with a French-language title was a number one hit in the UK for Irish girl band B*Witched, also reaching number nine on the US Billboard Hot 100?

C'est la Vie

Prize-winning Songs
QUESTIONS

1 Which singer and guitarist released the single *Tears in Heaven*, which went on to win Song of the Year at the 1993 Grammy Awards?

2 Which singer-songwriter wrote *Streets of Philadelphia* for the film *Philadelphia*, which went on to win the Academy Award for Best Original Song as well as four Grammys?

3 Which Canadian artist recorded *You're Still the One*, winning both the Grammy for Best Country Song in 1999 as well as that for Best Female Country Vocal Performance?

4 What is the title of the 1991 single recorded as a virtual duet between Natalie Cole and her father Nat King Cole, which won the Grammy for Record of the Year in 1992?

5 Which songwriter won the Grammy for Best R&B Song three times during the 1990s?

a. Rick James
b. R. Kelly
c. Lauryn Hill
d. Babyface

6 Which triple-Grammy-Award winning song by Santana and Rob Thomas topped the Billboard Hot 100 chart across the end of the 1990s into the beginning of 2000?

7 What song from the Disney film *Aladdin* won both a Grammy for Song of the Year and an Oscar for Best Original Song?

Prize-winning Songs

ANSWERS

1 Which singer and guitarist released the single *Tears in Heaven*, which went on to win Song of the Year at the 1993 Grammy Awards?

Eric Clapton

The success of Tears in Heaven *was bittersweet for Clapton, since he had written it about the tragic death of his four-year old son, Conor. Clapton wrote the lyrics for the first verse, but asked Will Jennings to write the remaining verses. Clapton later said that, "I almost subconsciously used music for myself as a healing agent, and lo and behold, it worked."*

2 Which singer-songwriter wrote *Streets of Philadelphia* for the film *Philadelphia*, which went on to win the Academy Award for Best Original Song as well as four Grammys?

Bruce Springsteen

3 Which Canadian artist recorded *You're Still the One*, winning both the Grammy for Best Country Song in 1999 as well as that for Best Female Country Vocal Performance?

Shania Twain

4 What is the title of the 1991 single recorded as a virtual duet between Natalie Cole and her father Nat King Cole, which won the Grammy for Record of the Year in 1992?

Unforgettable

5 Which songwriter won the Grammy for Best R&B Song three times during the 1990s?

a. Rick James
b. R. Kelly
c. Lauryn Hill
d. Babyface

d. Babyface

6 Which triple-Grammy-Award winning song by Santana and Rob Thomas topped the Billboard Hot 100 chart across the end of the 1990s into the beginning of 2000?

Smooth

7 What song from the Disney film *Aladdin* won both a Grammy for Song of the Year and an Oscar for Best Original Song?

A Whole New World

Solo Legends 2
QUESTIONS

1 What massively successful song is the lead single from Mariah Carey's 1994 album, *Merry Christmas*?

2 In which language did Celine Dion record her first eight albums, before her first English-language album release in 1990?

3 Which singer released the album *The Velvet Rope* in 1997, featuring the singles *Got 'til It's Gone* and *Together Again*?

4 For which 1998 animated film, based on the biblical story of Moses, did Whitney Houston and Mariah Carey record a version of the song *When You Believe*?

5 Rearrange the letters below to reveal the title of a 1996 song by George Michael, which spent several weeks at the top of the UK singles charts:

FAT VOLES (8)

6 Which highly successful rapper's real name is Marshall Bruce Mathers III?

7 What is the name of Madonna's first compilation album, released in 1990 and comprising some of her greatest hits as of its release?

Solo Legends 2
ANSWERS

1 What massively successful song is the lead single from Mariah Carey's 1994 album, *Merry Christmas*?

All I Want for Christmas Is You

The song was a success on its initial release, and has only continued to grow in popularity in subsequent years, having now topped the charts in over twenty-five different countries. In 2019 it went to number one on the US Billboard Hot 100 for the first time, repeating the same feat in 2020 with the UK singles chart. It is also the only Christmas song to have been certified diamond by the RIAA, indicating sales in excess of 10 million copies in the US.

2 In which language did Celine Dion record her first eight albums, before her first English-language album release in 1990?

French

3 Which singer released the album *The Velvet Rope* in 1997, featuring the singles *Got 'til It's Gone* and *Together Again*?

Janet Jackson

4 For which 1998 animated film, based on the biblical story of Moses, did Whitney Houston and Mariah Carey record a version of the song *When You Believe*?

The Prince of Egypt

5 Rearrange the letters below to reveal the title of a 1996 song by George Michael, which spent several weeks at the top of the UK singles charts:

FAT VOLES (8)

Fastlove

6 Which highly successful rapper's real name is Marshall Bruce Mathers III?

Eminem

7 What is the name of Madonna's first compilation album, released in 1990 and comprising some of her greatest hits as of its release?

The Immaculate Collection

R&B 2
QUESTIONS

1 Rearrange the letters below to reveal the name of a 1995 neo-soul album by singer-songwriter D'Angelo:

A BURN GROWS (5, 5)

2 Which singer, particularly known for her extensive vocal range, released the single *Hero* in 1993?

3 Which 1999 TLC track was accompanied by a futuristic music video that featured a large metal swing?

4 Which song released by Mark Morrison in 1996, and taken from his album of the same name, reached number one in the UK charts and number two on the Billboard Hot 100?

5 What was the title of Aaliyah's 1994 debut album, from which a single of the same name was released, as well as her debut single *Back & Forth*?

6 Which pop and R&B singer released the track *Un-Break My Heart* in 1996, winning her the Grammy for Best Pop Vocal Performance—Female?

7 Which musician released a self-titled debut album at the age of 15 in 1994, later experiencing worldwide success with the album *Confessions*?

1 Rearrange the letters below to reveal the name of a 1995 neo-soul album by singer-songwriter D'Angelo:

A BURN GROWS (5, 5)

Brown Sugar

> Brown Sugar *was the debut album for D'Angelo, achieving significant success by selling over two million copies, although he had previously written the hit single* U Will Know *for the R&B group Black Men United, which included Usher, R. Kelly, Boyz II Men and others, in the video for which he featured as the group's choir director.*

2 Which singer, particularly known for her extensive vocal range, released the single *Hero* in 1993?

Mariah Carey

3 Which 1999 TLC track was accompanied by a futuristic music video that featured a large metal swing?

No Scrubs

4 Which song released by Mark Morrison in 1996, and taken from his album of the same name, reached number one in the UK charts and number two on the Billboard Hot 100?

Return of the Mack

5 What was the title of Aaliyah's 1994 debut album, from which a single of the same name was released, as well as her debut single *Back & Forth*?

Age Ain't Nothing but a Number

6 Which pop and R&B singer released the track *Un-Break My Heart* in 1996, winning her the Grammy for Best Pop Vocal Performance—Female?

Toni Braxton

7 Which musician released a self-titled debut album at the age of 15 in 1994, later experiencing worldwide success with the album *Confessions*?

Usher

Grunge, Rock, & Punk 3

QUESTIONS

1 Which Bond theme, written by Paul and Linda McCartney, and which shares its title with the film it was featured in, was covered by Guns N' Roses in 1991?

2 What is the title of the Red Hot Chili Peppers song which opens with the lyrics, "Sometimes I feel like I don't have a partner"?

3 Featured on the *City of Angels* movie soundtrack, *Iris* was a 1998 hit for which alternative rock band from their album *Dizzy Up the Girl*?

4 Which singer and guitarist is the frontman for the band Green Day?

5 Tom DeLonge, Mark Hoppus, and Travis Barker have all been members of which Californian punk rock band?

6 Which 1991 song by Nirvana was accompanied by a music video set in a high school, with the band playing while accompanied by cheerleaders in a gymnasium?

7 Rearrange the letters below to reveal the name of a band fronted by Chris Cornell, who released the album *Superunknown* in 1994:

SUDDEN GROAN (11)

Grunge, Rock, & Punk 3

ANSWERS

1 Which Bond theme, written by Paul and Linda McCartney, and which shares its title with the film it was featured in, was covered by Guns N' Roses in 1991?

Live and Let Die

The Guns N' Roses version was included on their album Use Your Illusion I, *and went on to be nominated for the Grammy Award for Best Hard Rock Performance at the Grammy Awards in 1993. They decided to record the track after discovering in a late-night conversation that bandmembers Slash and Axl both loved the song.*

2 What is the title of the Red Hot Chili Peppers song which opens with the lyrics, "Sometimes I feel like I don't have a partner"?

Under the Bridge

3 Featured on the *City of Angels* movie soundtrack, *Iris* was a 1998 hit for which alternative rock band from their album *Dizzy Up the Girl*?

Goo Goo Dolls

4 Which singer and guitarist is the frontman for the band Green Day?

Billie Joe Armstrong

5 Tom DeLonge, Mark Hoppus, and Travis Barker have all been members of which Californian punk rock band?

blink-182

6 Which 1991 song by Nirvana was accompanied by a music video set in a high school, with the band playing while accompanied by cheerleaders in a gymnasium?

Smells Like Teen Spirit

7 Rearrange the letters below to reveal the name of a band fronted by Chris Cornell, who released the album *Superunknown* in 1994:

SUDDEN GROAN (11)

Soundgarden

Complete the Lyrics 2
QUESTIONS

Fill in the words missing from each lyric.

1 Sinéad O'Connor, *Nothing Compares 2 U*:

"It's been seven hours and _____ days
Since you took your love away"

2 The Cure, *Friday I'm in Love*:

"I don't care if Monday's _____
Tuesday's _____ and Wednesday too"

3 TLC, *Waterfalls*:

"Don't go chasing waterfalls
Please stick to the _____
and the _____ that you're used to"

4 *A Whole New World*, from *Aladdin*:

"I can show you the world
Shining, shimmering, _____"

5 Eagle-Eye Cherry, *Save Tonight*:

"Go on and close the curtains
All we need is _____"

6 Cher, *Believe*:

"Do you believe in _____ after _____?"

7 Madonna, *Vogue*:

"Look around, everywhere you turn is _____"

Complete the Lyrics 2
ANSWERS

Fill in the words missing from each lyric.

1 Sinéad O'Connor, *Nothing Compares 2 U*:

"It's been seven hours and _____ days
Since you took your love away"

Fifteen

> *Although* Nothing Compares 2 U *was a worldwide hit for Sinéad O'Connor, it was originally written by Prince for his band The Family, and was released on their album of the same name in 1984. O'Connor and her producer gave the song a very different arrangement, perhaps helping it become an international success.*

2 The Cure, *Friday I'm in Love*:

"I don't care if Monday's

_____

Tuesday's _____ and Wednesday too"

Blue; gray

3 TLC, *Waterfalls*:

"Don't go chasing waterfalls
Please stick to the _____
and the _____ that you're used to"

Rivers; lakes

4 *A Whole New World*, from *Aladdin*:

"I can show you the world
Shining, shimmering, _____"

Splendid

5 Eagle-Eye Cherry, *Save Tonight*:

"Go on and close the curtains
All we need is _____"

Candlelight

6 Cher, *Believe*:

"Do you believe in _____
after _____?"

Life; love

7 Madonna, *Vogue*:

"Look around, everywhere you turn is _____"

Heartache

One-hit Wonders 3
QUESTIONS

1 Which former R&B artist, now a born-again Christian pastor, was nominated for a Grammy Award for his song *This is How We Do It*?

2 Which band released the single *You Get What You Give* in 1998, generating some controversy over the name-dropping of several celebrities in the song's lyrics?

3 Which 1997 single, the lead release from his debut album *Desireless*, was written and recorded by Swedish artist Eagle-Eye Cherry and reached number five in the US Billboard Hot 100?

4 What is the title of the 1998 Semisonic single which features the Seneca-inspired lyric, "Every new beginning comes from some other beginning's end"?

5 Which primary color is also the title of a 1998 song by Italian band Eiffel 65, which found international success several years after its initial release?

6 Which one-man band wrote the 1997 single *Your Woman*, featuring a trumpet sample from the 1932 song *My Woman*?

7 Which 1990 song by MC Hammer borrows its musical introduction from the 1981 Rick James single, *Super Freak*?

One-hit Wonders 3

1 Which former R&B artist, now a born-again Christian pastor, was nominated for a Grammy Award for his song *This is How We Do It*?

Montell Jordan

Jordan parted with his long-term record label Def Soul in 2003 when they were reluctant to move away from his image as a "sex symbol." Montell, who had been happily married since before signing with the label, wished to focus more on his music. He subsequently left the music industry altogether and became a pastor at the Victory World Church in Atlanta, Georgia.

2 Which band released the single *You Get What You Give* in 1998, generating some controversy over the name-dropping of several celebrities in the song's lyrics?

New Radicals

3 Which 1997 single, the lead release from his debut album *Desireless*, was written and recorded by Swedish artist Eagle-Eye Cherry and reached number five in the US Billboard Hot 100?

Save Tonight

4 What is the title of the 1998 Semisonic single which features the Seneca-inspired lyric, "Every new beginning comes from some other beginning's end"?

Closing Time

5 Which primary color is also the title of a 1998 song by Italian band Eiffel 65, which found international success several years after its initial release?

Blue

6 Which one-man band wrote the 1997 single *Your Woman*, featuring a trumpet sample from the 1932 song *My Woman*?

White Town

7 Which 1990 song by MC Hammer borrows its musical introduction from the 1981 Rick James single, *Super Freak*?

U Can't Touch This

Pot Luck 3
QUESTIONS

1 Which 1999 song by Smash Mouth enjoyed increased popularity after featuring in the opening credits for the 2001 film *Shrek*?

2 Which 1976 hit by Stevie Wonder was sampled in Will Smith's 1999 hit *Wild Wild West*?

3 *Keep On Movin'* was a 1999 hit for which British boy band?

4 Who wrote and recorded *Doo Wop (That Thing)*, released in 1998, which was the musician's only solo US number one single on the Billboard Hot 100?

5 Which song, originally recorded by Billy Ocean, was covered by British band Boyzone in 1999, giving them a number one hit in the UK?

6 Which singer holds the record for the oldest female solo artist to top the Billboard Hot 100 for her 1998 hit, which was also the first pop song to feature Auto-Tune?

7 Which two singers recorded the duet *The Best Things in Life Are Free* for the 1992 film *Mo' Money*?

1 Which 1999 song by Smash Mouth enjoyed increased popularity after featuring in the opening credits for the 2001 film *Shrek*?

All Star

> The song was intended as an "anthem for outcasts," and before its use in Shrek it also featured in the film Mystery Men. Interestingly, it was only added to the album it was initially released on, Astro Lounge, at the last minute after Smash Mouth's record company felt that the album did not contain any potential singles.

2 Which 1976 hit by Stevie Wonder was sampled in Will Smith's 1999 hit *Wild Wild West*?

I Wish

3 *Keep On Movin'* was a 1999 hit for which British boy band?

Five

4 Who wrote and recorded *Doo Wop (That Thing)*, released in 1998, which was the musician's only solo US number one single on the Billboard Hot 100?

Lauryn Hill

5 Which song, originally recorded by Billy Ocean, was covered by British band Boyzone in 1999, giving them a number one hit in the UK?

When the Going Gets Tough, the Tough Get Going

6 Which singer holds the record for the oldest female solo artist to top the Billboard Hot 100 for her 1998 hit, which was also the first pop song to feature Auto-Tune?

Cher—for *Believe*

7 Which two singers recorded the duet *The Best Things in Life Are Free* for the 1992 film *Mo' Money*?

Luther Vandross and Janet Jackson

Singer-Songwriters 2
QUESTIONS

1 Which Canadian artist co-wrote and recorded the 1991 single *(Everything I Do) I Do It for You*?

2 Which song by British artist Des'ree begins with the lyrics, "Listen as your day unfolds / Challenge what the future holds"?

3 What is the one-word title of the 1998 Robbie Williams single which borrows musical themes from Nancy Sinatra's *You Only Live Twice*?

4 Which song by Dido appeared on her 1999 debut album after first being included in the soundtrack to the film *Sliding Doors*, and was later sampled by Eminem?

5 What is the title of the 1996 single by Welsh musician Donna Lewis which spent nine weeks at number two on the Billboard Hot 100, and also reached the top ten in the UK and Australia?

6 Two members of which American rock band played the guitar and bass for the recording of Alanis Morissette's hit song *You Oughta Know*?

7 Which artist wrote and recorded *Kiss From a Rose*, which was written in 1987 but not released until 1994 because they felt "embarrassed by it"?

Singer-Songwriters 2
ANSWERS

1 Which Canadian artist co-wrote and recorded the 1991 single
(Everything I Do) I Do It for You?

Bryan Adams

*(Everything I Do) I Do It for You was a number one hit
in around twenty countries, and to this day maintains its
unbeaten record of sixteen consecutive weeks at number
one in the UK singles chart. Selling more than 15 million
copies internationally, it is one of the best-selling singles
of all time—despite having apparently been written in just
45 minutes. It featured in the movie* Robin Hood: Prince of
Thieves, *clips from which appear throughout its music video.*

2 Which song by British artist
Des'ree begins with the lyrics,
"Listen as your day unfolds
/ Challenge what the future
holds"?

You Gotta Be

3 What is the one-word title of
the 1998 Robbie Williams single
which borrows musical themes
from Nancy Sinatra's *You Only Live
Twice*?

Millennium

4 Which song by Dido appeared
on her 1999 debut album after
first being included in the
soundtrack to the film *Sliding
Doors*, and was later sampled
by Eminem?

Thank You

5 What is the title of the 1996 single
by Welsh musician Donna Lewis
which spent nine weeks at number
two on the Billboard Hot 100, and
also reached the top ten in the UK
and Australia?

I Love You Always Forever

6 Two members of which
American rock band played
the guitar and bass for the
recording of Alanis Morissette's
hit song *You Oughta Know*?

Red Hot Chili Peppers

7 Which artist wrote and recorded
Kiss From a Rose, which was
written in 1987 but not released
until 1994 because they felt
"embarrassed by it"?

Seal

GAMES & TECH

GAMES & TECH

The 90s was the decade where technology was all that and a bag of (computer) chips. Where CDs, DVDs, and mass-produced mobiles hit the scene and video games graphics evolved from the 16-bit quality of a toddler's finger-painting to magical 3D worlds. Schoolyard throwdowns abounded over which gaming console was the ONLY one to own, and we had our first experiences of dial-up internet, chat rooms, text messages and the terrifying cuteness of Furby.

Do you have what it takes to (Palm) Pilot your way through this round, or has the cat Tamogotch-a tongue? Are you Doom-ed to fail or are you gonna nail it like a Tony Hawk Pro?

Mario
QUESTIONS

1 The first Mario platform game for the Super Nintendo (a.k.a. Super Famicom in Japan) was released in 1990. What was its name?

2 *Super Mario Land 3* sees the return of which similarly named arch-rival of Mario, introduced in the immediately preceding game in the series?

3 Which was the first Mario game to feature fully 3D gameplay, released in 1996?

4 In what 1998 video game, which saw an immediate sequel in 1999, do Mario, Luigi, Princess Peach, Yoshi, Wario, and Donkey Kong travel around an on-screen board game collecting stars?

5 Rearrange the following letters to reveal the title of an educational Mario product, first released for the PC in 1992, which features a pair of floating hands:

THE POETRY MAGICIANS (5, 7, 6)

6 *Super Mario Kart*, released in 1992, was the first game in the hugely successful Mario Kart series. How many different Mario characters were playable?

7 What was the subtitle of *Super Mario Land 2*, released for the Game Boy in 1992? The title refers to the items collected for beating each zone's boss.

1 The first Mario platform game for the Super Nintendo (a.k.a. Super Famicom in Japan) was released in 1990. What was its name?

Super Mario World

> *The game saw the introduction of Yoshi, a green dinosaur who Mario can ride in order to reach areas he can't otherwise access. A year later Yoshi then appeared in his own Tetris-like game, Yoshi, known as Mario & Yoshi in many territories.*

2 *Super Mario Land 3* sees the return of which similarly named arch-rival of Mario, introduced in the immediately preceding game in the series?

Wario

3 Which was the first Mario game to feature fully 3D gameplay, released in 1996?

Super Mario 64

4 In what 1998 video game, which saw an immediate sequel in 1999, do Mario, Luigi, Princess Peach, Yoshi, Wario, and Donkey Kong travel around an on-screen board game collecting stars?

Mario Party

5 Rearrange the following letters to reveal the title of an educational Mario product, first released for the PC in 1992, which features a pair of floating hands:

THE POETRY
MAGICIANS (5, 7, 6)

Mario Teaches Typing

6 *Super Mario Kart*, released in 1992, was the first game in the hugely successful Mario Kart series. How many different Mario characters were playable?

Eight

7 What was the subtitle of *Super Mario Land 2*, released for the Game Boy in 1992? The title refers to the items collected for beating each zone's boss.

6 Golden Coins

Home Consoles 1

1 What was the name of Sega's 8-bit handheld console, first released in Japan in 1990?

2 Atari also released a handheld console in Japan in 1990, although the North American version arrived first in late 1989. What was its name?

3 Which 1990s console launched with a controller that featured a square, triangle, circle, and X?

4 The 3DO was intended as a licensable CD-based game system which would be sold by various manufacturers, but it failed to catch on. The 3DO's founder, Trip Hawkins, was also the founder of which major video-game software company?

5 Sega had a staged release of the Megadrive/Genesis, culminating with its European release in 1990. How many lettered gameplay buttons were there on the bundled controller?

6 SNK Corporation released what expensive 1990 console, capable of playing almost identical versions of various arcade games of the time?

7 In the 1990s, Nintendo released the console whose name is often abbreviated to "SNES". What does that stand for?

Home Consoles 1
ANSWERS

1 What was the name of Sega's 8-bit handheld console, first released in Japan in 1990?

Game Gear

The Game Gear was developed to compete with Nintendo's hugely successful handheld Game Boy, featuring a full-color backlit screen which resulted in much better graphics than the Game Boy. The significant downside of this technical improvement, however, was that the Game Gear batteries lasted only a few hours at best, despite taking 6 AA batteries compared to the Game Boy's 4 AA batteries and 15-hour battery life.

2 Atari also released a handheld console in Japan in 1990, although the North American version arrived first in late 1989. What was its name?

Atari Lynx

3 Which 1990s console launched with a controller that featured a square, triangle, circle, and X?

Sony PlayStation

4 The 3DO was intended as a licensable CD-based game system which would be sold by various manufacturers, but it failed to catch on. The 3DO's founder, Trip Hawkins, was also the founder of which major video-game software company?

Electronic Arts

5 Sega had a staged release of the Megadrive/Genesis, culminating with its European release in 1990. How many lettered gameplay buttons were there on the bundled controller?

Three: A, B, and C

6 SNK Corporation released what expensive 1990 console, capable of playing almost identical versions of various arcade games of the time?

Neo Geo

7 In the 1990s, Nintendo released the console whose name is often abbreviated to "SNES". What does that stand for?

Super Nintendo Entertainment System

Pot Luck 1
QUESTIONS

1. Which successful Rockstar video game series, with a title relating to vehicle theft, saw its first release in 1997?

2. What is the subtitle of the first of the *Oddworld* video games?

3. What Nintendo 64 fighting game brought characters from a wide range of Nintendo franchises together?

4. What fighting game, infamous for its graphic violence, features a spoken phrase "Finish Him" at the end of its battles?

5. What 1993 Namco racing game was ported to the Sony PlayStation, becoming one of the most successful launch titles for the console?

6. Which Ubisoft platforming character is notable for his separately floating head, hands, body, and feet?

7. In which 1996 game for the Sega Saturn do players have to stop the evil Wizeman from destroying the world?

Pot Luck 1
ANSWERS

1 Which successful Rockstar video game series, with a title relating to vehicle theft, saw its first release in 1997?

Grand Theft Auto

The game was notable for its expansive open world in which players could drive wherever they wished, while completing missions and undertaking a range of optional extra activities. The first two games in the series used top-down views, later switching to full 3D views in later versions.

2 What is the subtitle of the first of the *Oddworld* video games?

Abe's Oddysee

3 What Nintendo 64 fighting game brought characters from a wide range of Nintendo franchises together?

Super Smash Bros.

4 What fighting game, infamous for its graphic violence, features a spoken phrase "Finish Him" at the end of its battles?

Mortal Kombat

5 What 1993 Namco racing game was ported to the Sony PlayStation, becoming one of the most successful launch titles for the console?

Ridge Racer

6 Which Ubisoft platforming character is notable for his separately floating head, hands, body, and feet?

Rayman

7 In which 1996 game for the Sega Saturn do players have to stop the evil Wizeman from destroying the world?

Nights into Dreams

Sonic the Hedgehog
QUESTIONS

1. What is the name of the ability, first introduced in the Megadrive/Genesis version of *Sonic the Hedgehog 2*, that allowed Sonic to move off quickly from a standing start?

2. How many chaos emeralds need to be collected in the original *Sonic the Hedgehog* in order to get the "good" ending?

3. What 1995 Sonic spin-off game, starring Knuckles, was released solely for Sega's ill-fated 32X Megadrive/Genesis expansion?

4. Which character joined Sonic as a central protagonist in *Sonic the Hedgehog 2*?

5. What was especially unusual about the original cartridge version of *Sonic & Knuckles*?

6. Sonic can smash televisions to gain power-ups. What appears on the screen of the TVs that allow him to temporarily run faster?

7. The first zone of the original Megadrive/Genesis Sonic the Hedgehog is the Green Hill Zone, but what was the name of the second zone?

Sonic the Hedgehog
ANSWERS

1 What is the name of the ability, first introduced in the Megadrive/ Genesis version of *Sonic the Hedgehog 2*, that allowed Sonic to move off quickly from a standing start?

Spin Dash, a.k.a. Super Dash Attack or Super Spin Dash

The ability to "rev" Sonic on the spot and send him off quickly was a significant improvement to the game, avoiding the need to sometimes torturously gain momentum by running backwards and forwards to build up speed. The Master System and Game Gear versions of Sonic the Hedgehog 2 *were developed separately, however, and did not gain the ability. Later ports of the original Megadrive/ Genesis* Sonic *have tended to add the option, however.*

2 How many chaos emeralds need to be collected in the original *Sonic the Hedgehog* in order to get the "good" ending?

Six

3 What 1995 Sonic spin-off game, starring Knuckles, was released solely for Sega's ill-fated 32X Megadrive/Genesis expansion?

Knuckles' Chaotix

4 Which character joined Sonic as a central protagonist in *Sonic the Hedgehog 2*?

Tails, a.k.a. Miles "Tails" Prower

5 What was especially unusual about the original cartridge version of *Sonic & Knuckles*?

It had a flap at the top which opened, into which you could insert the *Sonic the Hedgehog 3* cartridge in order to play an extended version of the game.

6 Sonic can smash televisions to gain power-ups. What appears on the screen of the TVs that allow him to temporarily run faster?

A red sneaker

7 The first zone of the original Megadrive/Genesis Sonic the Hedgehog is the Green Hill Zone, but what was the name of the second zone?

Marble Zone

Interactive Toys
QUESTIONS

1. Tamagotchi were digital pets that achieved enormous success during the second half of the 1990s, but what does "Tamagotchi" mean when translated into English?

2. Which handheld game encouraged you to quickly "Twist it!" and "Pull it!"?

3. Which virtual-pet rival to the Tamagotchi was released by Tiger Electronics in 1997?

4. Which cuddly, owl-like creatures, that were a must-have toy in 1998 and 1999, begin by speaking in their own invented language but then start to use more and more English words and phrases over time, as they "learn" your language?

5. Which novelty voice recorder was first featured in *Home Alone 2: Lost in New York* as a non-functional prop, but was later released as a working toy?

6. Which 1995 talking action figure, that had featured in a popular animated movie, included the phrases "I come in peace" and "To infinity, and beyond!"?

7. Which plush toy based on a Muppet character, that giggled when squeezed, became so heavily in-demand that it led to widely publicized shopping frenzies?

Interactive Toys
ANSWERS

1 Tamagotchi were digital pets that achieved enormous success during the second half of the 1990s, but what does "Tamagotchi" mean when translated into English?

Egg Watch

> *The handheld, egg-shaped devices featured a simple black-and-white display that owners interacted with using just three buttons. Starting from an on-screen egg, once it hatched the aim was to care for the digital creature by providing it as much—or as little—attention as you wished. The devices included various mini games to play, and you were responsible for feeding the digital pet on a regular basis.*

2 Which handheld game encouraged you to quickly "Twist it!" and "Pull it!"?

Bop It

3 Which virtual-pet rival to the Tamagotchi was released by Tiger Electronics in 1997?

Giga Pets

4 Which cuddly, owl-like creatures, that were a must-have toy in 1998 and 1999, begin by speaking in their own invented language but then start to use more and more English words and phrases over time, as they "learn" your language?

Furbies

5 Which novelty voice recorder was first featured in *Home Alone 2: Lost in New York* as a non-functional prop, but was later released as a working toy?

Talkboy

6 Which 1995 talking action figure, that had featured in a popular animated movie, included the phrases "I come in peace" and "To infinity, and beyond!"?

Buzz Lightyear

7 Which plush toy based on a Muppet character, that giggled when squeezed, became so heavily in-demand that it led to widely publicized shopping frenzies?

Tickle Me Elmo

Tomb Raider

QUESTIONS

1. The original release of *Tomb Raider* was initially exclusive in Europe to which 1990s console?

2. Which former UK video game development company created the original *Tomb Raider* game?

3. Who is credited with the initial concept of Lara Croft, and worked as lead artist on the first game?

4. What was different about the save capabilities of the PC version of the game?

5. What was notable about the use of music in the original *Tomb Raider* game?

6. The fourth *Tomb Raider* game was the first to include a subtitle in its name. What was that subtitle?

7. Which enormous, ancient creature chases Lara during the Lost Valley level of the original *Tomb Raider* game?

Tomb Raider
ANSWERS

1 The original release of *Tomb Raider* was initially exclusive in Europe to which 1990s console?

Sega Saturn

> The PlayStation and PC versions of the game followed shortly afterwards, while other platforms saw releases in later years. Subsequently, however, Sony signed a deal to keep the Tomb Raider games exclusive to the PlayStation until the year 2000.

2 Which former UK video game development company created the original *Tomb Raider* game?

Core Design

3 Who is credited with the initial concept of Lara Croft, and worked as lead artist on the first game?

Toby Gard

4 What was different about the save capabilities of the PC version of the game?

You can save at any point, not just using Save Crystals

5 What was notable about the use of music in the original *Tomb Raider* game?

It would only play occasionally, at selected moments, and otherwise the game had no music

6 The fourth *Tomb Raider* game was the first to include a subtitle in its name. What was that subtitle?

The Last Revelation

7 Which enormous, ancient creature chases Lara during the Lost Valley level of the original *Tomb Raider* game?

Tyrannosaurus Rex

Pot Luck 2
QUESTIONS

1. Which Naughty Dog platform game was developed as an exclusive for the Sony PlayStation, and featured a character who could spin to smash open crates?

2. Which futuristic anti-gravity racing game, published by Psygnosis, was a launch title for the PlayStation in Europe and North America?

3. Which side-scrolling Sega beat-em-up lets you play as one of Axel, Adam, or Blaze as you seek to defeat Mr. X?

4. What Sega-AM2 title was the first truly 3D fighting game ever released?

5. What color is the titular taxi in the Sega game, *Crazy Taxi*?

6. Which on-rails light-gun shooter game from Namco was ported from the arcade to the PlayStation in 1995, and is notable for its "cover system" in which the player can hide behind scenery to avoid getting shot?

7. In 1998, Konami introduced the first of which long-running series of rhythm games that requires players to move their feet in time with the on-screen music beats?

Pot Luck 2
ANSWERS

1 Which Naughty Dog platform game was developed as an exclusive for the Sony PlayStation, and featured a character who could spin to smash open crates?

Crash Bandicoot

The game was inspired by Nintendo's Mario and Sega's Sonic games, apparently with the intention of creating a competing character that was exclusive to the Sony console. Although the game never achieved an equivalent level of success, it did subsequently lead to many sequels.

2 Which futuristic anti-gravity racing game, published by Psygnosis, was a launch title for the PlayStation in Europe and North America?

Wipeout

3 Which side-scrolling Sega beat-em-up lets you play as one of Axel, Adam, or Blaze as you seek to defeat Mr. X?

Streets of Rage

4 What Sega-AM2 title was the first truly 3D fighting game ever released?

Virtua Fighter

5 What color is the titular taxi in the Sega game, *Crazy Taxi*?

Yellow

6 Which on-rails light-gun shooter game from Namco was ported from the arcade to the PlayStation in 1995, and is notable for its "cover system" in which the player can hide behind scenery to avoid getting shot?

Time Crisis

7 In 1998, Konami introduced the first of which long-running series of rhythm games that requires players to move their feet in time with the on-screen music beats?

Dance Dance Revolution

Home Consoles 2

1. The original 1994 PlayStation controller did not feature any control sticks, with just four buttons to press for controlling movement. What was the name of the 1997 PlayStation handheld controller which first added stick controls?

2. What was the name of Sega's last ever console, released during the 1990s, which was home to such titles as *Jet Set Radio* and *Crazy Taxi*?

3. Atari released which 1993 console that claimed to be 64-bit, although in reality its twin processors were both 32-bit chips?

4. What technology did the PlayStation introduce to make it easier to maintain game save data?

5. Nintendo briefly released an unusual 3D console in 1995, based around a bright-red plastic headset. What was its name?

6. Nintendo eventually followed up their hugely successful SNES with which console?

7. Which Sega console was the company's first full successor to the Megadrive/Genesis?

Home Consoles 2
ANSWERS

1 The original 1994 PlayStation controller did not feature any control sticks, with just four buttons to press for controlling movement. What was the name of the 1997 PlayStation handheld controller which first added stick controls?

Dual Analog Controller

The controller added not just one but two thumb-controlled analog sticks, which provided much finer controller in a wide range of games, and eventually became the standard control method for most games. Later this was superseded by the DualShock controller, which added in motors to provide force feedback as well as the ability to press down on the analog control sticks to activate hidden L3 and R3 buttons.

2 What was the name of Sega's last ever console, released during the 1990s, which was home to such titles as *Jet Set Radio* and *Crazy Taxi*?

Sega Dreamcast

3 Atari released which 1993 console that claimed to be 64-bit, although in reality its twin processors were both 32-bit chips?

Atari Jaguar

4 What technology did the PlayStation introduce to make it easier to maintain game save data?

Removable memory cards

5 Nintendo briefly released an unusual 3D console in 1995, based around a bright-red plastic headset. What was its name?

Virtual Boy

6 Nintendo eventually followed up their hugely successful SNES with which console?

Nintendo 64

7 Which Sega console was the company's first full successor to the Megadrive/Genesis?

Sega Saturn

Home Computers

1. Which hugely successful 1991 puzzle strategy game involved simultaneously guiding dozens of small green-haired creatures toward the exit?

2. Which 1992 game from iD software was one of the earliest and most influential first-person shooter games of all time, preceding their later game, *Doom*?

3. Which seminal 1993 interactive graphic adventure was developed on and first released for the Apple Mac, implemented using the HyperCard multimedia system?

4. Which sequel to the original *SimCity* was released in 1993, and saw a switch from the original overhead view to a new isometric perspective?

5. Which 1998 sci-fi video game, developed and published by Blizzard, went on to become an e-sports staple that is particularly successful in South Korea?

6. iD software followed up their hugely successful *Doom* with which 1996 game, introducing levels that included the true over/under 3D environments that *Doom* itself had lacked?

7. Valve were responsible for creating which 1998 game that saw the player take on the role of Gordon Freeman as he sought to escape the Black Mesa Research Facility?

Home Computers

1 Which hugely successful 1991 puzzle strategy game involved simultaneously guiding dozens of small green-haired creatures toward the exit?

Lemmings

> First published for the Amiga in 1991, but soon ported to many other platforms, the game was particularly designed to be played with a mouse, since it required the ability to rapidly move all around the screen to add and remove elements in order to prevent too many lemmings from being killed. The game's levels were split into Fun, Tricky, Taxing, and Mayhem sections.

2 Which 1992 game from iD software was one of the earliest and most influential first-person shooter games of all time, preceding their later game, *Doom*?

Wolfenstein 3D

3 Which seminal 1993 interactive graphic adventure was developed on and first released for the Apple Mac, implemented using the HyperCard multimedia system?

Myst

4 Which sequel to the original *SimCity* was released in 1993, and saw a switch from the original overhead view to a new isometric perspective?

SimCity 2000

5 Which 1998 sci-fi video game, developed and published by Blizzard, went on to become an e-sports staple that is particularly successful in South Korea?

StarCraft

6 iD software followed up their hugely successful *Doom* with which 1996 game, introducing levels that included the true over/under 3D environments that *Doom* itself had lacked?

Quake

7 Valve were responsible for creating which 1998 game that saw the player take on the role of Gordon Freeman as he sought to escape the Black Mesa Research Facility?

Half-Life

Pot Luck 3
QUESTIONS

1. Which arcade Namco fighting game, with a name that translates to "Iron Fist," was ported exclusively to the PlayStation in 1994?

2. In the Nintendo 64 game, *Banjo-Kazooie*, what kinds of animals are Banjo and Kazooie?

3. Which popular Nintendo 64 first-person shooter had the subtitle *Dinosaur Hunter*?

4. After releasing the 3D racing game *Virtua Racing* in 1992, Sega followed up with which hugely successful 1993 3D racing game which was later ported to the Saturn?

5. Which 1991 3D shooter game from Apogee Software gained notoriety thanks to its casual depiction of various risqué topics within the game?

6. What 1990 action space-flight simulation game, developed by Origin Systems, sees the player flying a *Bengal*-class Strike Carrier?

7. What was the name of the titular earthworm in a side-scrolling platform game from Shiny Entertainment?

Pot Luck 3
ANSWERS

1 Which arcade Namco fighting game, with a name that translates to "Iron Fist," was ported exclusively to the PlayStation in 1994?

Tekken

The game was one of the first to use full 3D animation, as opposed to a series of 2D sprites, for its combat action. The franchise went on to be hugely successful, with several sequels and even spin-off feature films, and was particularly well-regarded for its subtle gameplay mechanics.

2 In the Nintendo 64 game, *Banjo-Kazooie*, what kinds of animals are Banjo and Kazooie?

A bear and a bird, respectively

3 Which popular Nintendo 64 first-person shooter had the subtitle *Dinosaur Hunter*?

Turok: Dinosaur Hunter

4 After releasing the 3D racing game *Virtua Racing* in 1992, Sega followed up with which hugely successful 1993 3D racing game which was later ported to the Saturn?

Daytona USA

5 Which 1991 3D shooter game from Apogee Software gained notoriety thanks to its casual depiction of various risqué topics within the game?

Duke Nukem

6 What 1990 action space-flight simulation game, developed by Origin Systems, sees the player flying a *Bengal*-class Strike Carrier?

Wing Commander

7 What was the name of the titular earthworm in a side-scrolling platform game from Shiny Entertainment?

Earthworm Jim